THE

UNIVERSITY CHALLENGE

QUIZ BOOK

OVER 1000 QUESTIONS FROM THE TV SERIES

BBC BOOKS

This book is published to accompany the *University Challenge* television series which is produced for BBC Television by Granada Television in association with College Bowl Inc. and based on a format owned and copyrighted by College Bowl Company Inc.

Published by BBC Books, an imprint of
BBC Worldwide Publishing,
BBC Worldwide Limited, Woodlands,
80 Wood Lane, London W12 OTT

First published 1995

ISBN 0 563 37194 3

Edited by Gareth Williams

Printed by Martins the Printers Ltd, Berwick upon Tweed
Bound by Hunter & Foulis Ltd, Edinburgh
Cover printed by Clays Ltd, St Ives plc

*The front cover photograph shows the teams from the University of Aberdeen (top)
and the University of Birmingham.*

Contents

FOREWORD

I first thought about creating *University Challenge* while playing basketball at McGill University in Montreal, Canada during the late 1930s. I loved playing basketball, it was exciting, competitive and entertaining for those watching. But one day I realized that not everyone could develop into a star athlete and it didn't matter. What did matter, and was far more important, was the development of the mind and almost everyone, given the opportunity, could reach those heights. So I set about developing *University Challenge*, a different kind of 'sport' that everyone could participate in – a game with all the elements, except for the ball, that made basketball so exciting. Instead of the ball there are questions. There are two teams, each representing a different university and a host or moderator acting as a referee. The host tosses up a starter question for both teams worth 10 points and the team that answers it correctly earns a bonus question worth a stated number of points. The questions cover a wide range of subjects from maths, science and sports to literature, philosophy and general knowledge. The team with the most points at the end of the game is the winner (see How to Play the Game on page 5).

University Challenge is not only exciting and entertaining, it highlights the value of education to millions of people of all ages all over the world. Bamber Gascoigne hosted the show for many years in England and today's *University Challenge* host on the BBC is Jeremy Paxman. The game has won numerous awards throughout the world, including an Emmy award and the prestigious Peabody award for Outstanding Achievement in the Field of Education and Entertainment, a rare accomplishment.

University Challenge is timeless. Knowledge is an ever-growing facet of one's life and I think young people and adults appreciate *University Challenge*, the varsity sport of the mind, as much as any athletic competition.

Don Reid,
Creator of *University Challenge*,
the Varsity Sport of the Mind

A BRIEF HISTORY OF UNIVERSITY CHALLENGE

The first episode of *University Challenge* was originally broadcast on 21 September 1962. It was a match between the universities of Manchester and Leeds. The host was Bamber Gascoigne, the programme's inimitable questionmaster until 1987, when the show went off air.

University Challenge returned to the screen in 1994 for the twenty-fourth series with a new look and a new presenter in the form of Jeremy Paxman.

HOW TO PLAY THE GAME

University Challenge is usually played with two teams of four people. Obviously, this can vary depending on the number of people who want to play. The game consists of starter questions and bonus questions. Starter questions are worth 10 points each and may be answered, without conferring, by any of the players. Contestants may interrupt the questionmaster as he is reading the question. However, if an incorrect answer is given after interrupting, 5 points are lost and the question is offered to the opposing team who may pick up the points.

After a starter question has been answered correctly, that team then has the chance of picking up an additional 15 points from the bonus questions, which are usually in sets of 3, worth 5 points apiece. Bonus questions are not handed over to the opposing team if they are answered incorrectly.

At the end of each game in this book, there are five spare starter questions in the event that neither of the teams is able to answer a given starter.

The game lasts for a predetermined length of time and the winning team is the one with the highest score at the close of play.

Game one

1

YOUR STARTER FOR
Who, in 1993, became the eighth woman and the first African-American woman to win the Nobel Prize for Literature?

Geography
a Which capital city lies on almost the same latitude as Sydney and faces it across the Pacific Ocean?
b Which capital city lies on roughly the same latitude as San Francisco and faces it across the north Pacific Ocean?
c Which capital city lies almost on the same line of longitude in the Mediterranean Sea as Algiers?

2

YOUR STARTER FOR
Which Greek school of philosophy was founded by Zeno of Citium around the end of the fourth and the beginning of the third century BC?

Philosophy
a Which branch of philosophy is concerned with human conduct and values and the nature of right wrong?
b Which seventeenth-century philosopher was expelled by the Jewish community of Amsterdam in 1656 for his heretical thinking?
c Scotsman David Hume influenced the development of two modern philosophical schools, one was scepticism, what was the other?

3

YOUR STARTER FOR
Which day of the week is named after the Earth's only natural satellite?

Plane figures
Identify the plane figures in each case.
a It can be converted into a rectangle by cutting a right-angled triangle off one end and sliding it to the opposite end.
b A conic section formed by the intersection of a cone by a plane parallel to its side.
c It comprises a quadrilateral having two parallel sides of unequal length.

4

YOUR STARTER FOR 10

Which screen personality, who was portrayed in a 1992 film by Robert Downey Junior, first went to America with the Fred Karno Company, a Vaudeville organization, before being signed up by the Keystone Film Company to make slapstick one-reelers?

Musical terms

a Which word, Italian for detached, describes a method of playing a note so that it is shortened and thus 'detached' from its successor?

b Which term used in musical scores is synonymous with ritardando, meaning to hold back or slow down gradually?

c What name is given to the pedal on an organ that gradually brings into action all the stops?

5

YOUR STARTER FOR 10

What is next in this series of numbers: 1, 18, 4, 13?

Place names

a What did the word chipping mean, as used in English place names such as Chipping Norton and Chipping Campden?

b Many Scottish and Irish place names began with the letters 'Kil', for example, Kilkenny or Kilmarnock. What did 'Kil' usually mean?

c The old English word 'burna' is responsible for the endings of place names such as Eastbourne, Sherbourne and Pangbourne. What did this ending signify?

6

YOUR STARTER FOR 10

Born of a Sardinian father and a Spanish mother, which sportsman grew up, in his own words, 'in a cave near Marseille' and, after a journey via Auxerre, Marseille, Bordeaux and Leeds, joined Manchester United in November 1992?

Mother and daughter actresses

a Which actress was once the stepdaughter of Elizabeth Taylor and later the wife of a hugely successful singer-songwriter?

b The mother of which actress was the 'victim' in a legendary Hitchcock shower scene?

c The female lead in the Hitchcock films *The Birds* and *Marnie* is the mother of which film actress?

7

YOUR STARTER FOR

In which narrative musical work is the hero represented by a string quartet, a bird by a flute, a duck by an oboe, the cat by a clarinet and the wolf by three horns?

BONUS QUESTIONS

Ancient Egypt and archaeology

a In which year did the British Museum stage a Tutankhamen exhibition to celebrate the fiftieth anniversary of the tomb's discovery by Howard Carter?

b Much of Howard Carter's early training came from which British archaeologist, with whom he first went to Egypt in 1890?

c Which pharaoh, who reigned for much of the thirteenth century BC, reigned for a short time as co-ruler with his father Seti the first?

8

YOUR STARTER FOR

In the parliamentary passage of a bill, what follows the report stage?

BONUS QUESTIONS

Art

a Which Flemish artist, best known for a portrait that hangs in the Wallace Collection in London, also painted *Banquet of the Officers of the St George Militia Company* in 1616?

b Romantic artist Eugène Delacroix was a friend of which lovers, both of whom he painted in 1838?

c Two of John Constable's favourite subjects were the mills owned by his father; some were in Flatford in Suffolk, where in Essex were the others?

9

YOUR STARTER FOR

In which great battle were the two opposing leaders born in the same year – this was the only occasion that they met in war, and the last battle that either of them fought. The victor was aged 46 and the loser was 45. The loser died six years later in 1821.

BONUS QUESTIONS

Animal products

a Formerly much used in the manufacture of perfumes to maintain their fragrance, ambergris is a grey, waxy substance derived from the intestines of which mammal?

b Used in ointments and in soap, lanolin is a waxy material occurring naturally in which animal product?

c Consisting of the myricyl ester of palmitic acid, free cerotic acid and other homologues, which white or yellow plastic substance is used in polishes and in the shaping of waxwork models?

10 **YOUR STARTER FOR**

Conchiglie meaning shells, pappardelle meaning nests, and farfalle meaning butterflies are all types of what?

Computer languages

a What general term is used for computer programming languages in which instructions, sometimes expressed as words in English, correspond to several machine code instructions, examples being 'fortran', 'basic' and 'pascal'?

b Which procedure-orientated language was developed in 1959, originally to meet the needs of business programming?

c Which language, introduced at Bell Laboratories in 1974, was originally developed for use in the UNIX operating system?

11 **YOUR STARTER FOR**

The portion of an estate that remains after payment of debts, funeral and testamentary expenses, legacies, administration costs, etc., is called what?

Accents

a What name is given to the character printed under a letter 'C' in French to show that is pronounced like 'S' rather than 'K'?

b What name is given to the sign put over an 'N' in Spanish, which gives it a 'nya' pronunciation?

c What name is given to the mark placed over a vowel in some languages to indicate the omission of a letter or the rising or fall of the voice on a vowel or syllable?

12 **YOUR STARTER FOR**

Harold Abrahams, who was Chairman of the Amateur Athletic's Board from 1948–68, was the first Britain to win a gold medal in which Olympic event?

Teeth

a Of which teeth does a human being have two in each quadrant and because of their two cusps they are alternatively known as bicuspids?

b What name is given to the slightly spongy and very sensitive bone-like substance in a tooth?

c Which branch of dentistry deals with the care of the gums and other structures supporting the teeth?

13 YOUR STARTER FOR

Which animator created the characters Wallace and Grommit?

Sporting trophies

a Which sporting trophy, presented by the grandfather of George Bush and bearing his name, was first competed for in 1922?

b Which sporting trophy is named in honour of the nineteenth-century schoolboy who had little regard for the rules of football?

c Which sporting trophy has been won once by Oxford University although never by Cambridge, twice by old boys of Eton College and once by old boys of Charterhouse?

14 YOUR STARTER FOR

What is the result of positive phototropism?

Books of the Bible

a Which book of the Bible has a Hebrew title meaning 'In the Wilderness' because it focuses on the Israelites during their 40 years of wandering after their departure from Egypt?

b Only two books of the Bible are named after women. For 5 points can you name both?

c Which book of the Bible tells of the slaying of Goliath by David?

15 YOUR STARTER FOR

Certain species of which animal are noted for their ability to kill poisonous snakes by darting at the head and cracking the skull with a powerful bite?

Industrial processes

a Who, in 1856, developed and patented a process of mass-producing steel by removing impurities from pig iron by a blast of air into the molten material?

b In the simplest form of the process, what is added to rubber in vulcanization?

c Which German chemists gave their names to a process for the conversion of coal into liquid fuels similar to crude oil used in Germany during World War II?

16

YOUR STARTER FOR 10

Which field of physics was initiated when the correct mathematical description of the thermal energy radiated from a black-body was formulated by Max Planck in 1900?

BONUS QUESTIONS

'Dwarfs'

a In Charles Dickens' *The Old Curiosity Shop,* what is the name of the dwarf from whom Little Nell's grandfather borrows money?

b In the television series *Red Dwarf,* who plays the role of Dave Lister?

c Which is the only one of the Seven Dwarfs to wear glasses?

17

YOUR STARTER FOR 10

Where, according to Coleridge, 'did Kubla Khan/A stately pleasure dome decree'?

BONUS QUESTIONS

Abdications

a Why did Belgium's King Baudouin abdicate for 24 hours in April 1990?

b Who was British Prime Minister at the time of the abdication crisis of Edward VIII?

c Which ruler of The Netherlands abdicated on 4 September 1948 because of ill-health?

18

YOUR STARTER FOR 10

In 1900, Edward Henry published his findings on the identification and classification of what?

BONUS QUESTIONS

Geology

a In geology, what name, derived from the Spanish for 'cauldron', is given to a volcanic crater of great size?

b What name, derived from the Spanish for 'table' is given to a flat-topped hill found in desert regions?

c What name, derived from the Spanish for 'cord', is given to a chain of mountains such as the Andes?

19

YOUR STARTER FOR 10

What term was coined in 1952 by art critic Harold Rosenberg to describe activities such as riding a bicycle over the canvas, practised by abstract expressionists such as Jackson Pollock?

Colours

a Which word, which has come to mean an expert or enthusiast, derives from the colour of the coats worn by part-time fire fighters in nineteenth-century New York?

b Where would Pinkie Brown and Rose together make a literary seaside confection?

c Who was *The Times'* war correspondent who described the British lines at Balaclava as 'this thin red streak tipped with a line of steel'?

20 YOUR STARTER FOR

Which term in chess comes from the Persian for 'King' and 'dead'?

Numbers

a Which German mathematician, a contemporary of Newton, was a great advocate of the binary number system, for whom '1' stood for God and '0' stood for the void?

b In the hexadecimal number system, how is the number 15 written?

c What name is applied to any number such as a fraction that can be expressed as the ratio of two integers?

SPARE STARTER QUESTIONS

21 Why are flags flown on public buildings on 6 February?

22 What name is given to the point on a planet's orbit when it is furthest from the sun?

23 In diving, what does the acronym 'scuba' stand for?

24 In 1905, New York police arrested the cast of a Shaw play for 'disorderly conduct'. What was the play?

25 Which piano concerto was given its first performance in Leipzig in 1811, with Friederich Schneider as soloist? It was the only one that the composer himself did not play in public as, by that time, he was too handicapped by his deafness.

Game two

1

YOUR STARTER FOR

Who said 'I can forgive Alfred Nobel for having invented dynamite, but only a fiend in human form could have invented the Nobel Prize'?

BONUS QUESTIONS

Musical festivals

a The annual music festival at Aldeburgh in Suffolk, established in 1948 with assistance from Sir Peter Pears and others, was inspired by which English composer, conductor and pianist who died in 1976?

b The Bavarian city of Bayreuth stages festivals dedicated to the works of which composer, a resident there from 1872 until 1883?

c Staged mainly in their respective cathedrals, the annual choral and orchestral performance, known as the 'Three Choirs Festival', is held in turn at which three cities?

2

YOUR STARTER FOR

What is the result of subtracting the temperature difference between the boiling and freezing points of water on the Celsius scale from their difference on the Fahrenheit scale?

BONUS QUESTIONS

The Commonwealth

a Which Commonwealth country calls itself a 'Co-operative Republic' in its official title?

b Which European country left the Commonwealth in 1949?

c Which country left the Commonwealth in 1972, but rejoined in 1989?

3

YOUR STARTER FOR

In 1993, Europe's earliest human remains, estimated to be 500 000 years old, were uncovered in Essex. What name was given to this find?

BONUS QUESTIONS

Prayer

a Which hymn of praise, incorporated into evening prayer in Western churches, is found in Luke I, verses 46–55?

b Which religion uses a device called a prayer wheel, each revolution of which represents one repetition of the prayers?

c Who wrote the novel *A Prayer For Owen Meany*, published in 1989?

4

YOUR STARTER FOR

Which national hero, who, according to legend, was ordered by Gessler, the Duke of Austria's steward, to perform an act of great marksmanship, is the subject of Rossini's last opera?

Clocks

a Claimed to be the world's oldest working clock, dating from 1386 or earlier, it has no face and chimes the hours. In which English cathedral can it be found?

b Which Dutch astronomer and physicist's interest in the accurate measurement of time led him to the discovery of the pendulum as a regulator of clocks as described in his *Horologium* of 1658?

c Which element, first used in a clock in 1929, has so increased the accuracy of timekeeping that an observatory clock will typically have a maximum error of a few ten-thousandths of a second per day, equivalent to one second every ten years?

5

YOUR STARTER FOR

Who won an Oscar for best actress in the 1980s, over 20 years after she had topped the singles charts as a singer?

Grammar

a In grammar, which tense, denoting an action completed prior to some specified or implied past point of time, is expressed in English by 'had' and the past participle?

b Which case denotes the indirect object of a verb as in the German 'Sie gaben ihr Wein' (they gave her wine)?

c In the English language, what term is used for a noun with the ending '-ing' formed from a verb and having some of the qualities of a verb?

6

YOUR STARTER FOR

Which early twentieth-century artistic movement acquired its name because the work of its founders was likened to wild beasts?

Literary and sporting doctors

a Which consultant neurologist is better known to the general public for his historic sporting achievement of 6 May 1954?

b Which Gloucestershire doctor was the first president of the English Bowling Association, but is best remembered for his achievements in another sport?

c Which medical man, who in 1890 gave up his practice to concentrate on a literary career, claimed the wicket of Dr Grace at Crystal Palace in 1900?

7 YOUR STARTER FOR 10

Who, as the Labour Party's candidate, unexpectedly won the Irish presidential election in 1990, becoming the first woman to hold the post?

 BONUS QUESTIONS

Model villages

a What is the name of the 'model village' in Dorset to which the Prince of Wales has devoted much time?

b Which model village was built by the soap millionaire William Hesketh Lever and named after one of his most successful products?

c Which social reformer created a model community in New Lanark, where he established the first infant school in Britain in 1816?

8 YOUR STARTER FOR  10

What material, commonly used as a type of fastening, was invented by Swiss inventor Georges de Mestral after studying why burrs stuck to his trousers and noticing that they were made of thousands of tiny hooks?

 BONUS QUESTIONS

Guerilla organizations

a The rebel Farabundo Marti National Liberation Front operates in which country?

b Which right-wing organization was founded by soldier and revolutionary Jonas Savimbi?

c Abimael Guzman, arrested in September 1992, was the leader of which Communist guerilla organization?

9 YOUR STARTER FOR  10

The daughter of Zeus and Leda and wife of the Spartan King Menelaus, which beauty of Greek legend was abducted by Paris, Prince of Troy?

 BONUS QUESTIONS

Dramatic terms

a What term is used for a type of monologue in which an actor addresses an audience by speaking his thoughts aloud?

b Sometimes used at the end of acts in nineteenth-century melodrama and farce, what word describes a representation formed by living persons caught in static attitudes?

c John Milton's play *Comus* of 1634 is described as what type of performance, combining as it does poetic drama, music, dance, lavish costume and costly stage effects?

10 **YOUR STARTER FOR**
In economics, which term, coined in the 1970s, specifically describes a situation in which there is no growth in the economy, but inflation continues to rise?

BONUS QUESTIONS **The word 'new'**
a Which fashion designer launched his 'New Look' in spring 1947?
b Who bought a house named New Place in May 1597?
c Which bird did Wordsworth describe as a 'blithe New-comer'?

11 **YOUR STARTER FOR**
Who was responsible for the architecture of the oldest surviving Renaissance theatre in Italy at Vicenza?

BONUS QUESTIONS **Sound**
a What name is given to waves, such as sound waves, where the vibration or displacement takes place in the direction of travel of the waves?
b In music, what is the effect of doubling the frequency of the fundamental component of a note?
c Which measure of comparing sound intensities is equal to 'ten log-to-the-base-10 I (eye) over I (eye) nought', where 'I' is the intensity of the sound under consideration and 'I (eye) nought' is the intensity of a reference sound?

12 **YOUR STARTER FOR**
How many prime numbers occur between 20 and 30?

BONUS QUESTIONS **Art**
a London's National Gallery contains Philippe de Champaigne's triple portrait of which seventeenth-century French statesman?
b In 1635, which court painter produced a triple portrait of British monarch Charles I?
c *Three Studies for Figures at the Base of a Crucifixion* was painted by which British artist?

13

YOUR STARTER FOR 10

Hardy borrowed the words 'far from the madding crowd' from Gray's Elegy, but which two words complete the line in the poem?

BONUS QUESTIONS

Church windows

a Who designed Coventry Cathedral's baptistery window intended to suggest the love of God flowing into the world?

b Daresbury Parish Church in Cheshire has a stained glass window commemorating the author and characters of which children's book published in 1865?

c During the seventeenth century, whose troops destroyed most of the stained glass at Peterborough?

14

YOUR STARTER FOR 10

Which saint in the Middle Ages was believed to have curative powers and for this reason his name was applied to a particular kind of convulsive neurological disease, chorea? Sufferers attended his chapels in the hope of a cure.

BONUS QUESTIONS

Sporting arenas

a Which game has a playing area with maximum dimensions of 62 feet 10$1\frac{1}{16}$ of an inch (19.7 metres) in length by 42 inches (107 centimetres) in width?

b Which game is played on a grass field with maximum dimensions of 200 yards by 300 yards?

c Which game has a playing area of 9 feet by 5 feet, with its upper surface 30 inches above the floor?

15

YOUR STARTER FOR 10

Which isotope of carbon is used in the radioactive dating of objects that contained wood or materials made from plants?

BONUS QUESTIONS

Jazz trumpeters

a Whose creole jazz band did Louis Armstrong join in Chicago in 1922, developing a unique dual-cornet style with him that was a feature of many of their recordings?

b Which trumpeter, who, with Charlie Parker, was a formative influence on Bebop, later made rock-orientated albums and included the Cyndi Lauper hit 'Time After Time' on his 1985 album *You're Under Arrest*?

c Which contemporary jazz trumpeter has also made several classical albums and, in 1984, became the first instrumentalist to win two simultaneous Grammy Awards in the Jazz and Classical categories?

16

YOUR STARTER FOR

Which Arab leader, born in a tent in the desert in 1942, espoused a form of Islamic socialism that he expounded in his *Green Book,* published in two volumes in 1976 and 1980?

The heart

a For the measurement of what would a medical practitioner use a sphygmomanometer (sfigg-momanometer)?

b Blood pressures are typically recorded as a maximum and minimum reading; what name is given to the pressures corresponding to these readings?

c Which Czech physiologist who, in 1839, created the first independent Department of Physiology at the University of Breslau, gives his name to the fibrous tissue that conducts the pacemaker stimulus along the inside walls of the ventricles to all parts of the heart?

17

YOUR STARTER FOR

Which group, taking their name from the caption beside a Madonna poster, in 1994 became the first act ever to have four singles enter the charts at number one?

Robberies

a Which famous painting was stolen from a national gallery in 1994, only to be recovered two months later?

b What was stolen from Westminster Hall in March 1966?

c For the theft of what was Vincenzo Perugia sentenced to one year, 15 days imprisonment in 1914?

18

YOUR STARTER FOR

Mounted upon steeds coloured white, red, black and pale, the allegorical figures, said in Revelations to represent conquering, war, famine, and pestilence or death, are generally known by which name?

Ancient history

a Which King of Sparta was killed in 480 BC after defending the pass of Thermopylae against the Persian army of Xerxes I?

b Which Roman politician and businessman, who crushed the Spartacus uprising of 71 BC, formed the first Triumvirate with Julius Caesar and Pompey in 60 BC and was killed by the Parthians at the Battle of Carrhae (ka-rye) in 53 BC?

c Which Greek soldier, historian and writer, born about 430 BC, served under King Agesilaus II (A-gee-silayus) of Sparta for which he was rewarded with an estate near Olympia in Elis?

19 YOUR STARTER FOR

Who, in 1977, was awarded the Booker Prize for his novel *Staying On*, a sequel to his *Raj Quartet*?

BONUS QUESTIONS

Museums
What is the main theme of each of the following London museums?
a The Wellcome Institute.
b Bethnal Green Museum.
c Apsley House, Hyde Park Corner.

20 YOUR STARTER FOR

What word, in mathematics, can mean an arrangement of elements into rows and columns; in biology, substance between cells; and, in geology, the material in which, for example, gem stones are embedded?

BONUS QUESTIONS

Chess champions
a Who was deprived of his World Chess Championship in 1975 when he refused to defend it against Anatoly Karpov?
b Who, when he defeated Karpov in 1985, became the youngest ever world chess champion?
c Which Briton lost to Kasparov in an unofficial world championship contest in London in 1993?

SPARE STARTER QUESTIONS

21 Who, after a brief marriage to Margaret Kempson, showed a predilection for the name by marrying Margaret Roberts in 1951, becoming the father of twins in 1953?

22 'Man is born free; and everywhere he is in chains' is the opening of which work by Jean Jacques Rousseau, published in 1762?

23 What was discovered by mathematical computation at the Lowell Observatory in 1930?

24 Which city in Tennessee is said to have been named after one of ancient Egypt's capitals because its location on the Mississippi suggested that of its historic namesake on the Nile?

25 What is defined as the ratio of the speed of a fluid or body to the local speed of sound?

Game three

1
YOUR STARTER FOR 10
Which building , destroyed by fire in AD 64 during the reign of Nero, was rebuilt by the Emperor Vespasian and completed by his son Titus?

BONUS QUESTIONS

Sociology
a What term did the French sociologist Emile Durkheim coin in his study of suicide to refer to a condition of instability resulting from a breakdown of standards and values or from lack of purpose and ideals?

b What term is used to describe the type of family, more common in advanced industrial societies, consisting of husband, wife and immature children, which forms a unit apart from the rest of the community?

c Which German term, meaning 'community', is contrasted with 'Gesellschaft' (association) as contrasting types of social organization?

2
YOUR STARTER FOR 10
Clement Attlee, Clint Eastwood, Alf Roberts and Michael Henchard have all held which civic post?

BONUS QUESTIONS

Former African colonies
a Which African Republic was a French colony from the 1890s, when it was known as French Sudan, and, after a brief federation with Senegal, achieved complete independence in 1960?

b Which African kingdom was known as Basutoland until it achieved independence from Britain in 1966?

c In which former Portuguese colony, which became fully independent in 1975, are the largest ethnic groups the Ovimbundu and the Mbundu?

3
YOUR STARTER FOR 10
Which fruit flavouring is added to the Belgian Lambic beer to make Kriek-Lambic?

Universities

a Which European seat of learning was founded in the mid thirteenth century as a theological college, was named after its founder and did not admit secular students until the nineteenth century?

b Which seat of learning was founded in 1861 but moved to its present, Cambridge site in 1916?

c Which American University, in New York State, was established in 1754 as Kings College?

4 YOUR STARTER FOR

What is the name of the valley near Dusseldorf that gave its name to the important anthropological discovery made there in 1856?

Works inspired by Shakespeare

a Which 1966 play 'borrowed' two peripheral characters from a Shakespearean tragedy as the central characters for a successful stage comedy?

b On which Shakespearean tragedy was the 1985 Akira Kurosawa film *Ran* based?

c Which operatic working of a Shakespearean tragedy was first performed in Russia in 1934 and, after condemnation by *Pravda*, was withdrawn from the stage?

5 YOUR STARTER FOR

Which Simone De Beauvoir treatise, published in 1949, was an early inspiration for the women's movement?

Economists

a Whose work *The General Theory of Employment, Interest and Money,* published in 1936, advocated a remedy for recession based on a government-sponsored policy of full employment?

b Which German economist in his book *Small is Beautiful: Economics as if People Mattered*, published in 1973, makes a case for small-scale economic growth without great capital expenditure?

c Which Austrian-born economist, who became a British citizen in 1938 and who was noted for his criticism of the Welfare State, wrote *The Road to Serfdom*, in which he argues that government intervention in a free market can lead to the economic disaster that can pave the way for a totalitarian takeover?

6

YOUR STARTER FOR

Following the Whitbread Round The World Race, who was named Yachtsman Of The Year in January 1989?

American religious movements

a What is the popular name for the members of the religious group that was founded in the United States in 1830 by Joseph Smith Junior and has the official name of the Church of Jesus Christ of Latter-Day Saints?

b A work entitled *Science and Health with Key to the Scriptures,* is the textbook of which religious denomination, established in the USA in 1879?

c Who graduated from the Florida Bible Institute in 1940 and Wheaton College in 1943 and had become widely regarded as fundamentalism's chief spokesman by the 1950s, organizing large-scale preaching tours?

7

YOUR STARTER FOR

Which mountain has two summits called Kibo and Mawenzi?

Film making

a What was the name of the British film maker who died in 1972 and who created the documentary film, a term he himself coined?

b Which French name is applied to the technique of film making that utilizes raw, natural sound, hand-held cameras and little rehearsal, used to great effect by Richard Leacock and other film makers?

c What is meant by the term 'film à clef'?

8

YOUR STARTER FOR

Who is the only British party leader this century to have won four general elections, his first victory being against Sir Alec Douglas-Home and his last being against Edward Heath?

Elections

a In which year was the so-called Khaki Election held?

b Why was the 1918 General Election given the name 'The Coupon Election'?

c In the 1918 General Election, who was the only woman elected?

9 **YOUR STARTER FOR**

Which scientific theory was first promulgated in Edward Lorenz's paper 'Does the Flap of a Butterfly's Wings in Brazil Set Off a Tornado in Texas'?

BONUS QUESTIONS

Opera

a Which musical instrument protected the operatic character Tamino from evil?

b Which operatic heroine is stabbed to death by her spurned lover just outside the stadium where his rival for her affections competed?

c In which opera, which was premièred at La Scala on 25 April 1926, is a whole city on sentence of death commanded to find the name of an unknown prince?

10 **YOUR STARTER FOR**

Which Lennon-McCartney song features 'Tangerine trees and marmalade skies'?

BONUS QUESTIONS

Nineteenth-century European peace treaties and conferences

a What name was given to the Polish territory granted to Russia by the Congress of Vienna?

b The demilitarization of which sea was agreed at the Congress of Paris in 1856?

c After which assembly did Disraeli claim that he had brought back 'Peace...with honour' and Bismarck boast that he had 'Driven Europe four-in-hand'?

11 **YOUR STARTER FOR**

Which European country, with a population of nearly 7 million, has only 1600 active military personnel, but 565 000 army reservists?

BONUS QUESTIONS

Mountain ranges

a Which mountain range, forming a natural continental boundary between Europe and Asia, extends 2000 miles south from the Kara Sea, the highest point being some 6000 feet above sea level?

b Which mountain range is an extension of the Himalayas into the Hindu Kush and serves as a watershed for the basins of the Indus and Tarim Rivers?

c In which range of mountains is the Roncesvalles Pass?

12

Which suffix, which in most cases has arisen from the local usage to distinguish a Royal Manor, appears in the names of 12 places in England?

Alternative medicine

a Which alternative medical therapy was developed in the nineteenth century by the American physician Andrew Taylor Still?

b Which part of the body is massaged in the technique known as reflexology?

c Which system of medicine was first developed by the German physician Samuel Hahnemann?

13

Which term, more commonly used to describe the style of some post-impressionist painters, can refer to musical passages where the notes seem to be in 'dots' rather than in melodic phrases?

Ladies

a In Arthurian legend, what was the name of the 'Lady of the Lake'?

b What is the date of Lady Day?

c In *The Five Nations*, Kipling borrowed the title of a Wordsworth poem, 'Our Lady Of The Snows', to describe which country of the British Empire?

14

In which Evelyn Waugh novel did Paul Pennyfeather assert that 'Anyone who has been to an English public school will always feel comparatively at home in prison'?

Celebrated court cases

a Accused by Ruskin in 1877 of 'Flinging a pot of paint in the public's face', which American artist sued for damages and won a farthing?

b Charged as 'an evil-doer and a curious person, searching into things under the earth and above the heaven; and making the worse appear the better cause, and teaching all this to others', which Athenian philosopher, condemned at his trial in 399 BC, refused a fine, drank hemlock and died?

c *J'accuse*, Zola's fierce attack on the French judiciary of the day, was motivated by a miscarriage of justice in the case of which Jewish artillery officer?

15 YOUR STARTER FOR 10
What is the cubed root of 512?

Sad demises of literary heroines
a Who throws herself under his departing train after she sees her lover, Captain Vronsky, saying goodbye to another woman?
b Who is arrested at Stonehenge and later hanged for the murder of her seducer, Alec?
c Which doctor's wife committed suicide by taking arsenic, after being refused money by a lover?

16 YOUR STARTER FOR 10
In what respect did an engineer supersede a soldier in 1990, a scientist succeed a playwright in 1991 and a banker replace an architect in 1994?

Scottish football
a In November 1991, Gretna became the first Scottish club for 104 years to play in the first round of which English sporting competition?
b Which is the only club in the Scottish football league to play its home games in England?
c Which British football manager has led both an English and a Scottish team to success in the European Cup Winners' Cup?

17 YOUR STARTER FOR 10
The Rodgers and Hart musical *The Boys From Syracuse* was based on which Shakespeare play?

Bees
a To which order of insects do bees belong?
b What type of creature is a bee-eater?
c 'Where the bee sucks, there suck I' is sung in which Shakespeare play?

18 YOUR STARTER FOR 10
What word, which may mean the minimum required level of production, particularly in a planned economy, more usually refers to an imposed limit on the quantity of goods produced, purchased or imported?

Ancient Roman history
a Following the expulsion of Ancient Rome's last king in the early sixth century BC, what title was given to the two annually elected highest magistrates?

b Which Roman statesman and scholar was elected consul in 63 BC?

c Cicero was executed in 43 BC. Name one of the members of the second triumvirate who ordered his execution.

19 YOUR STARTER FOR

What, in cricketing terms, is 'a pair of spectacles'?

Ballet

a Which Warsaw-born dancer joined the Diaghilev Ballet in 1913, became a British citizen in 1918 and, in 1935, gave her name to a ballet company?

b Which Scotsman, knighted in 1983, was Director of the Royal Ballet from 1970 to 1977 before becoming its Principal Choreographer?

c British choreographer Sir Frederick Ashton created the 1963 ballet *Marguerite and Armand* for which two leading dancers?

20 YOUR STARTER FOR

In Einstein's mass-energy equation E = MC squared, what does the constant 'C' represent?

The United Nations

a How many permanent members sit on the United Nations Security Council?

b In total, how many members make up the full Security Council?

c Which member state was expelled from the UN in 1971?

SPARE STARTER QUESTIONS

21 Which seventeenth-century statesman was known as 'L'Eminence Rouge', or 'The Red Eminence'?

22 Which organization, founded by Bertrand Russell and Canon John Collins in 1958, arranged the Aldermaston Marches, which took place during the late 1950s and 1960s?

23 Nicknamed Marshal Forwards, which Prussian Field Marshal, born at Rostock in 1742, joined Wellington at Waterloo to complete the defeat of Napoleon?

24 Which basic condiment from South-East Asia, made from a variety of bean, with wheat, water and salt added, is called shoyu in Japan and jiang yong in China?

25 Which organ of the body contains approximately one million nephrons?

Game four

1

YOUR STARTER FOR

Which creation of Jerome Siegal and Joseph Shuster first appeared in edition number one of Action Comics in June 1938?

Presidents

a Which African politician, who lost power in May 1994 after 31 years as his country's Prime Minister and President, worked as a GP in London until 1953?

b Which Asian politician, one of the most influential Communist leaders of the twentieth century and his country's President from 1954 until his death in 1969, worked as a gardener, street sweeper, waiter and oven-stoker during the six years he spent in France from 1917–23?

c A chemist and the first President of his country from 1949–52, he was a scientist at Manchester University and helped the British munitions industry during the First World War by devising a process to extract acetone from maize; who was he?

2

YOUR STARTER FOR

The Edda is a body of two thirteenth-century collections of which country's early poems and mythologies?

Shipwrecks and castaways

a Who was the Scottish sailor whose experiences on the island of Juan Fernandez formed the basis of Defoe's *Robinson Crusoe*?

b Which British navigator was cast adrift in the bay named after him by mutineers in 1611, never to be seen again?

c On which island is St Paul's Bay, reputedly near the place where St Paul was shipwrecked in AD 60?

3

YOUR STARTER FOR

In physics and mathematics, what name is given to any quantity that requires a direction as well as a magnitude to specify it completely?

Classical music in films

a Which 1979 American comedy film opens to George Gershwin's *Rhapsody in Blue*?

b Who wrote the score for the 1948 film *Scott of the Antarctic,* later transforming it into his seventh symphony?

c Mozart's Clarinet Concerto for Orchestra in A is featured in which Oscar-winning film released in 1985?

4 YOUR STARTER FOR

What name is given to a tract of the western desert in Egypt where very soft sand makes it virtually impassable to vehicles and which protected the left flank of the Allied Armies before and during the Battle of Alamein in 1942?

Counties

a Yorkshire and Lincolnshire were for centuries divided into administrative areas known as ridings. Which Irish county is divided into ridings?

b Which English county was divided into six areas known as rapes?

c For centuries, Kent was divided into five administrative areas. What were these called?

5 YOUR STARTER FOR

What did Keats describe as 'Thou still unravish'd bride of quietness/Thou foster-child of silence and slow time'?

Sequences to continue or complete

a Who is next in this sequence: Smyslov, Botvinnik, Tal, Botvinnik, Petrosian?

b Complete this sequence: Pye, Southey, Wordsworth, Tennyson?

c Who is next in this sequence: Pacelli-Roncalli, Montini, Luciani?

6 YOUR STARTER FOR

Which technique of producing three-dimensional images, using a highly coherent beam of light or other radiation, was conceived in 1947 by Hungarian-born electrical engineer Dennis Gabor?

Carriers of disease

a Epidemic typhus is spread from person to person by what?

b Which disease is usually contracted by working, bathing or swimming in water populated by snails that carry the small, parasitic flatworms called blood flukes responsible for the disease?

c What, in Africa, transmits sleeping sickness?

7 YOUR STARTER FOR

Neil Young's lyric 'It's better to burn out than fade away' was quoted in which rock star's suicide note of April 1994?

BONUS QUESTIONS

Novels with Latin American connections

a Which novel by D. H. Lawrence is set in Mexico?

b In the novel by Graham Greene, what was the occupation of Jim Wormold, 'Our Man in Havana'?

c Which Nobel Prize-winning novelist created the fictional Colombian village of Macondo?

8 YOUR STARTER FOR

Three US states have shorelines on Lake Superior: Michigan, Minnesota and which other?

BONUS QUESTIONS

War, literature and cinema

a The action of Ernest Hemingway's novel *For Whom The Bell Tolls* takes place during which war?

b Which novel by Erich Maria Remarque, dealing with the First World War, was published in 1929?

c During which war is D. W. Griffith's classic film *The Birth of a Nation* set?

9 YOUR STARTER FOR

As the parliamentary day begins and the Speaker's procession makes its way through the central lobby, what is shouted by the duty policemen?

BONUS QUESTIONS

Legal terms

a What title is given to a paid, professional, full-time magistrate with functions similar to those of a Justice of the Peace?

b What word describes an addition to a bill in the form of a new clause or a recommendation added by a jury to their verdict?

c What term describes an authority given by one person to another to act legally for them in their absence, perhaps to convey land, receive debts or sue?

10 YOUR STARTER FOR

Which book's first chapter contains this extract: 'With a suitcase full of clothes and underwear in my hand, and an indomitable will in my heart, I set out for Vienna...I too hoped to become "something" '?

BONUS QUESTIONS

Sporting rock stars

a Which sailing fanatic was airlifted from his yacht, *Drum*, after it overturned during a race in October 1985?

b Which piano-playing singer-songwriter reputedly acquired his broken nose while a local welterweight boxing champion?

c Which heavy metal vocalist was ranked within the top 20 British men's foilists in 1989, and with his team, Hemel Hempstead Fencing Club, represented Britain in the European Club Championships that year?

11 YOUR STARTER FOR

What numerical result do you get if you add the number of bits in a byte to the number of bytes in a kilobyte?

BONUS QUESTIONS

Unfamiliar or less familiar names

a Which office was held by Severinus, Donus and Conon in the seventh century?

b Where in Britain during the summer months could you encounter Rosanna, Seaford United and Perth City on a weekly basis?

c What are Tebet, Shebat or Sebat and Adar?

12 YOUR STARTER FOR

The cockle shell, worn by pilgrims on their hats, is the symbol of which saint, whose shrine in Spain is one of the holiest places in Christendom?

BONUS QUESTIONS

Taxes

a Which tax was first levied in England in 1222 to finance the campaign in the Holy Land?

b A tax on what was introduced in England in 1689 to replace the unpopular hearth tax?

c In 1973, VAT replaced two existing taxes. One was Purchase Tax, what was the other?

13 YOUR STARTER FOR

On a standard typewriter keyboard, which letter occurs between 'S' and 'F'?

Pop music

a Which American pop group has a name synonymous with the stage of sleep when dreams occur?

b Who was the lead singer with the group ABC, formed in Sheffield in 1980?

c Which country music singer performed guest vocals on the KLF's hit 'Justified and Ancient'?

14 YOUR STARTER FOR

In the 1860s, French chemist Hippolyte Mege-Mouries first produced which foodstuff from animal fats, although it is now made mainly from vegetable oils?

Religion

a Which religion's most sacred books contain the teachings of Mahavira?

b Adherents of which religion believe that Ormuzd, the good god, is in perpetual conflict with Ahriman, the evil god?

c With which religious movement would you associate the ideas of Marcus Garvey?

15 YOUR STARTER FOR

Mendelssohn's Third Symphony, inspired by a visit to Holyrood House, and nicknamed the 'Scottish', is dedicated to whom?

Placename translations

a Which US state's capital, lying 21 degrees north and 157 degrees west, has a name meaning 'sheltered bay'?

b 'Muddy river mouth' is the literal translation of the name of which city and federal territory of Malaysia?

c Which large city of Eastern Africa, lying approximately 6 degrees south and 39 degrees east, has a name derived from the Arabic for 'haven of peace'?

16 YOUR STARTER FOR

If you were 60 degrees north and 25 degrees east you would be a few kilometres from the centre of which capital city?

Parts of flowers

a What name is given to the upper two-lobed part of a plant stamen, each lobe containing two pollen sacs within which are numerous pollen grains?

b What is the name of the sticky surface at the tip of the carpel of a flower, which receives the pollen?

c The modified leaves that comprise the calyx of a flower are known as what?

17 YOUR STARTER FOR 10

What final number is produced if the following are added together: the number of fates in classical mythology, T. E. Lawrence's 'Pillars of Wisdom' and the number of muses?

Sporting puzzles

a Starting and finishing on a double, what is the least number of darts needed to score 301?

b How many cue strokes does a snooker player make in scoring a break of 147?

c Theoretically, what is the minimum number of strokes a player can make to win a set at lawn tennis?

18 YOUR STARTER FOR 10

Which low-velocity artillery firearm, with a shorter barrel and a larger bore than a gun, but a smaller bore and longer barrel than a mortar, takes its name from the Dutch for catapult and was widely used in the First World War?

Afternoons

a Whose poem was the inspiration for Debussy's *Prélude à l'Après-Midi d'un Faune*?

b What was the subject of Ernest Hemingway's book *Death in the Afternoon*?

c Which band's 1966 chart-topping single 'Sunny Afternoon' tells how the singer's girlfriend has returned to her Ma and Pa, 'telling tales of drunkenness and cruelty'?

19 YOUR STARTER FOR 10

Which painter, who rejected impressionism during the 1880s, had a son, Jean, who became a film director – his best-known pre-war works being *La Grande Illusion* and *Les Règles du Jeu*?

Numeric names or terms

a Which numeric term was applied to the extremist religious sect of the Cromwellian period, which was led by Harrison and Venner among others?

b Which battle was known as the Battle of the Three Emperors?

c What numeric name is given to the eroded chalk cliffs on the Sussex coast between Cuckmere Haven and Beachy Head?

20 YOUR STARTER FOR

Which official ceremony was performed by George VI in July 1948, Prince Philip in November 1956, and Her Majesty the Queen in July 1976?

Fiction set in India

a Salman Rushdie's Booker Prize-winning novel *Midnight's Children* is set in which Indian city?

b An alleged 'incident' in the Marabar caves is a central theme in which 1924 novel, later made into a film?

c The rape of Daphne Manners in the Bibigar Gardens was a central and recurring theme in which award-winning TV series first transmitted in February 1984?

SPARE STARTER QUESTIONS

21 Which cathedral town did Trollope use as the basis for his fictional Barchester?

22 The name of which navigator has been given to two satellite galaxies of the Milky Way because his crew discovered them during the first voyage round the world?

23 The leaves of which wild flower, whose English name comes from the French for 'lion's tooth', are used in a salade de pissenlit au lard in France?

24 Which cud-chewing hoofed mammal, found in the rain forests of Central Africa, and unknown to science until about 1900, is the only other member of the giraffe family?

25 Who commanded the Spartan forces at the Battle of Aegospotami in 405 BC?

Game five

1

YOUR STARTER FOR
What name is given to the rise or fall of a liquid in, for example, a tube of small cross-sectional area?

BONUS QUESTIONS **American Indians**
a Warriors from which North American Indian nation were massacred by the US 7th Cavalry at the Battle of Wounded Knee in 1890?
b Which American Indians of Arizona and New Mexico live in circular huts, usually made of logs and mud, called hogans?
c Which American Indian people were evicted from their homes in Georgia in the winter of 1838 and forced to march to Oklahoma in what became known as 'the trail of tears'?

2

YOUR STARTER FOR
Which Middle-Eastern capital city has given its name to a fruit, a fabric, a metal and a variety of rose?

BONUS QUESTIONS **Philosophers**
a Which English philosopher and political theorist wrote that in times of war the life of man is 'solitary, poor, nasty, brutish and short'?
b Which philosopher was the first to expound the theory of utilitarianism in *Fragment on Government* and *An Introduction to the Principles of Morals and Legislation*?
c Which philosopher and economist founded the Utilitarian Society in 1823, taking the word from *Annals of the Parish*, a novel of country life by John Galt.

3

YOUR STARTER FOR
In which port did the mutiny on the battleship *Potemkin* take place during the Russian Revolution of 1905?

BONUS QUESTIONS **Plantagenets**
a Which king, who reigned from 1154–1189, is considered by most historians to be the first Plantagenet king?
b How did the Plantagenets get their name?

c In the 'Palliser' novels by Anthony Trollope, what position does Plantagenet Palliser, Duke of Omnium, reach as indicated by the title of the fifth book of the series?

4

YOUR STARTER FOR

Speed specifies the rate at which an object moves, but what term is used for the vector quantity which additionally specifies direction of motion?

Diaries

a Who wrote a diary entitled *Five Years of my Life* in which he recorded the experiences of his unjust imprisonment at the turn of this century?

b Whose last entry in his diary began 'every day we have been ready to start for our depot 11 miles away'?

c In which city did Zlata Filipovic write a diary that she began just before her eleventh birthday?

5

YOUR STARTER FOR

Pope John Paul II, Julio Iglesias, Albert Camus and Billy the Fish have all played which position at football?

Great tenors

a Which tenor, born in Naples in 1873, who had a recording career that lasted from 1902 until 1920, gave his last performance at the Metropolitan Opera House on Christmas Eve 1920?

b Which tenor, born near Ancona in 1890, made his Metropolitan Opera House début as Faust in Boito's *Mefistofele* in 1920, and, from 1946, often appeared in operas with his daughter Rina, making his last concert appearance in 1955?

c Which tenor, born in Modena in 1935, made his professional début as Rodolfo in *La Bohème* in Reggio Emilia in 1961?

6

YOUR STARTER FOR

Sussex, Dorking, Leghorn, Rhode Island Red and Buff Orpington are standard breeds of which domesticated bird?

Languages

a Which native Swiss language is spoken by about 1 per cent of the population of Switzerland?

b Which European language, the origin of which is a mystery, is called Euskara in its own language?

c Which Mediterranean language is the only form of Arabic to be written in the Latin script?

7

YOUR STARTER FOR

Viennese physician Dr Franz Josef Gall, born in 1758, gave what name to his theory, discredited by modern science, that measurable psychological and intellectual features can be revealed by skull shape?

Islands

a Of which island did Britain take over the administration in 1878, annexing it in 1914 and finally granting it independence in 1960?

b Which island was occupied by Britain during the war of the Spanish succession, seized by France during the Seven Years War, restored to Britain by the Treaty of Paris, and finally conceded to Spain by the Peace of Amiens in 1802?

c Which island was ruled by Venice until the fall of the Venetian Republic in 1797 and under the protection of Britain from 1815–1864, when it was ceded to Greece, the cricket pitch in its capital city being a legacy of British rule?

8

YOUR STARTER FOR

Who, when he took 9 wickets for 57 runs in the Test against South Africa at the Oval in August 1994, achieved the sixth best test match bowling figures of all time?

Bishops

a Prior to his consecration as Archbishop of Canterbury, of which diocese was Dr Carey the bishop?

b Three bishops of the Church of England have an automatic right to sit in the House of Lords. The Bishop of London is one. Who are the other two?

c Two bishops of the Church of England are not eligible to sit in the Lords. One is the Bishop of Gibraltar. Who is the other?

9

YOUR STARTER FOR

How many strings has a mandolin?

Birds

a To which family of birds does the American road runner belong?

b Birdcage Walk in St James's Park, Westminster is so named because of the aviaries kept there by which king?

c The Egyptian god Horus had the head of which bird?

YOUR STARTER FOR 10

One of the greatest libraries of the ancient world was founded in about 300 BC, repeatedly damaged by fire throughout its existence and was eventually destroyed in the seventh century AD. In which city was it?

BONUS QUESTIONS

Green

a The Arthur Wood composition Barwick Green is one of the most familiar pieces of music of BBC Radio. Why?

b Which Shakespearean character says 'O! Beware my Lord of jealousy, it is the green-ey'd monster...'?

c How did the fruit the greengage acquire its name?

YOUR STARTER FOR 10

Why are lich-gates in churchyards so called?

BONUS QUESTIONS

British prime ministers

a Seven of Britain's last ten prime ministers were graduates of Oxford University. Who was the last Cambridge graduate to occupy Number 10?

b Who was the last prime minister to have represented a Scottish constituency during his parliamentary career?

c Who was the only prime minister to die at Number 10?

YOUR STARTER FOR 10

Which guerilla leader was born in Argentina in 1928, served in several government posts in Castro's Cuba and, in 1966, moved to Bolivia where he was killed leading a guerilla group?

BONUS QUESTIONS

Saints

a Which Englishman was canonized in 1935, 400 years after his execution?

b Which Englishman was canonized by Pope Alexander III in 1161?

c Saint Augustine was the first Archbishop of Canterbury. Who succeeded him?

13 YOUR STARTER FOR 10

According to Genesis, which land lay to the 'East of Eden'?

Pre-Raphaelite painters

a In 1855, the English artist William Holman-Hunt, a prominent member of the Pre-Raphaelite Brotherhood, completed which work depicting a solitary animal on the shores of the Dead Sea?

b During the 1850s, Elizabeth Siddal was introduced into the Pre-Raphaelite circle, serving at first as a model for the whole group, but, in 1860 marrying which of its members?

c Pre-Raphaelite Sir John Everett Millais used the sea wall at Budleigh Salterton, on the Devon coast, as the setting for a painting of whose 'boyhood'?

14 YOUR STARTER FOR 10

What are the solano of southern Spain, the zonda of Argentina, the brickfielder of Australia, the Mistral of Southern France and the sirocco originating in North Africa?

Novels

a Which novel is narrated by Lockwood, the temporary tenant of Thrushcross Grange, and then taken up by Nelly Dean, a house-keeper?

b The events of which novel are told in the 'Letters of the Heroine' and 'Lovelace', written to Anna Howe and John Belford, respectively?

c Which novel is set at the Marcia Blaines School for Girls in Edinburgh during the 1930s?

15 YOUR STARTER FOR 10

After being entirely redesigned by the American architect I. M. Pei, which museum's Richelieu wing opened in November 1993?

Law

a Which division of the High Court deals with matters such as matrimonial disputes, adoption and wardship?

b Give the name of both divisions of the Court of Appeal.

c What word describes an order of the court, in the nature of a prohibition, by which the prohibited party is ordered not to do, or to cease from doing, some act, even though that act does not amount to a crime, non-compliance with which constitutes contempt of court?

16 **YOUR STARTER FOR**
Which African country is due east of Rio de Janeiro?

English cathedrals

a Which cathedral, probably founded by St Etheldreda in the seventh century, the present Norman building dating from the end of the eleventh century, stands on rising ground near the River Ouse?

b The building of which cathedral, designed by John Francis Bentley, was begun in 1895, the greater part being completed in the early 1900s?

c Which futuristic cathedral was consecrated in 1967, only six years after construction of all but the Great Crypt had begun?

17 **YOUR STARTER FOR**
Which two words refer to a style of French cooking that avoids traditional rich sauces, emphasizing instead fresh ingredients with attractive presentation?

Nobel Prizes

a Why are Nobel Prizes awarded on 10 December?

b A Nobel Prize is often shared between more than one winner, but under what circumstances may two Nobel Prizes be awarded in a single field in one year?

c The sixth Nobel Prize was first awarded in 1969 in what field?

18 **YOUR STARTER FOR**
His younger brothers, Lenin and Vladimir, are respectively an engineer and a businessman in their native Venezuela. Under what name is Ilich Ramirez Sanchez, deported from the Sudan to France in August 1994, better known?

Giants of myth, legend and literature

a In Greek mythology, the first-born children of Uranus and Gaea and their descendants, noted for their enormous size and strength and ultimately cast into Tartarus, were known collectively by which name?

b In British legend, which two giants were taken as prisoners to London and made to do duty at the royal palace on the site of the Guildhall, where their effigies stand?

c Father and son, Gargantua and Pantagruel, are giants whose riotous adventures are recorded by which sixteenth-century French satirist, writing under the anagrammatical pseudonym Alcofri Bas Nasier?

19

YOUR STARTER FOR

Darryl Jones, who has played with Miles Davis and Sting, replaced whom as bass player with the Rolling Stones in July 1994?

Fabrics

BONUS QUESTIONS

a Which word, meaning of poor quality or badly made, is derived from a type of reconstituted woollen fibre that was manufactured around Dewsbury in Yorkshire?

b Which fine, smooth, woollen yarn takes its name from the Norfolk village where the fabric was traditionally woven?

c Which fine, silken fabric, traditionally used in veils and dresses, takes its name from the French town famous for its production, which is the capital of Corrèze Département?

20

YOUR STARTER FOR

Which concept of reasoning around and about a problem, rather than making a direct approach along a single, conventional channel, was originated by Edward De Bono in the mid 1960s?

Astronomy

BONUS QUESTIONS

a During what event would brilliant points of light known as Baily's Beads be seen?

b What would we call an event in which Mercury or Venus, as seen from the Earth, crosses the face of the sun?

c Which seventeenth-century German astronomer reached the conclusion that the Earth and planets travel about the sun in elliptical orbits?

SPARE STARTER QUESTIONS

21 Formed in 1970 and abolished in 1983, what popular name was given to the central policy review staff, the consultative body set up to provide cabinet ministers with informed advice on policy decisions?

22 Which period of geological time occurred approximately 360–285 million years ago, its name referring to the immense amount of coal formation taking place at that time?

23 Three English cities have passport offices: London, Liverpool and which other?

24 The powers of which English king were substantially reduced by the provisions of Oxford in 1258 and, six years later, by the Mise of Lewes?

25 Which artistic movement was founded in Zurich in 1916 and included Arp and Duchamp among its pioneers?

Game six

1

YOUR STARTER FOR

Which city fits the following description? A lake port with a population of over 600 000, it was settled by large numbers of German immigrants in the nineteenth century and, consequently, became a centre for the brewing industry. It is the largest city in the state of Wisconsin.

BONUS QUESTIONS

Craftsmen and designers

a The craftsman Thomas Tompion, who worked closely with Robert Hooke, inventor of the hair spring, is most famous for making what?

b For the manufacture of what has the London-based company of James Purdey been renowned for almost 200 years?

c If you were given a Staunton Set, what would you do with it?

2

YOUR STARTER FOR

Anne Hyde was the mother of which two British monarchs?

BONUS QUESTIONS

Planets

a Which planet, with a mean surface temperature of about 460 degrees Celsius, is the hottest in the solar system?

b What word, derived from the Latin for 'white', is used for the ratio of the amount of solar radiation reflected by a planet to the amount incident upon it?

c Which planet, with an axial inclination of about 98 degrees, effectively rotates on its side?

3

YOUR STARTER FOR

Which alkaloid, extremely toxic in its pure form, occurs in the tobacco plant and is named after a sixteenth-century French diplomat who introduced the plant to France?

BONUS QUESTIONS

Sport

a The oldest trophy that can be won by professional athletes in North America is named after Lord Stanley of Preston, a former Governor General of Canada, and is competed for in which sport?

b What are the names of the two conferences into which the professional game of American football has been divided since 1970?

c The American men's basketball team won the 1992 Olympic title.
Which country, competing in their first Olympics as an independent
state, did they beat in the final?

4 YOUR STARTER FOR **10**

Based on a story by Prosper Mérimée, what was the title of Bizet's last
opera, whose music was used for a Broadway musical, later filmed, in
which Escamillo the Toreador became Husky Miller, a boxer.

Statues

a Christ of the Andes, a 26-foot-tall bronze statue erected in 1904 at
the summit of the Uspallata Pass, symbolizes peace between which
two countries?

b Where would you see statues carved from volcanic stone and known
as Moai (mo-eye)?

c Sir George Frampton's statue of Peter Pan stands in which of
London's parks?

5 YOUR STARTER FOR **10**

What was based in Weimar from 1919 to 1925, in Dessau until 1932,
in Berlin until its closure in 1933 and was founded by the German
Architect Walter Gropius?

Mottoes

a Which organization, established in 1924, has a Latin motto that
translates as 'art for art's sake'?

b Which order of chivalry, established in 1725, has as its motto 'tria
juncta in uno', or, 'three joined in one'?

c What is the motto of the Olympic movement?

6 YOUR STARTER FOR **10**

There are three national parks in Wales. The Pembrokeshire Coast and
Snowdonia are two, what is the third?

Royal marriages

a For what reason did Henry II of England imprison his wife, Eleanor
of Aquitaine, between the years 1174 and 1189?

b Who became the third husband of Mary, Queen of Scots in 1567?

c Who secretly married the Prince of Wales (later George IV) in 1785, being known by her name from her second marriage seven years previously?

7 YOUR STARTER FOR **10**

Which mammal was unknown to Europeans until the Jesuit missionary Armand David discovered some skins in 1869 and was not seen by a European until nearly 50 years later?

Trees

a The longbow was first used in the twelfth century when it was made of elm, but, as the weapon developed, the wood of another tree was used. Which tree?

b Which native British tree is sometimes called 'the Judas Tree'?

c After which battle did Charles II reputedly hide in the Boscobel Oak?

8 YOUR STARTER FOR **10**

Which novel, first published in 1871–2, begins, 'Miss Brooke had the kind of beauty which seems to be thrown into relief by poor dress'?

Medical abbreviations

a The debilitating condition often referred to as 'Yuppie Flu' is sometimes abbreviated to ME. What does ME stand for?

b Medically, what do the initials IVF stand for?

c The subject of litigation in recent years, what is RSI?

9 YOUR STARTER FOR **10**

What is the name of the lace scarf worn by Spanish women over their hair and shoulders?

International organizations

a Two South American countries are members of OPEC. Venezuela is one. What is the other?

b Which country became a member of NATO in 1952 and joined the European Community in 1981?

c Which international organization was established in 1923 and has its headquarters in Lyon?

10 YOUR STARTER FOR **10**

Which metallic element is obtained from the ore stibnite, hence the origin of its chemical symbol 'SB'?

Writers' houses

a Which writer lived at 24 Cheyne Row, Chelsea, for almost 50 years, until his death in 1881?

b Lamb House in Rye contains personal possessions and memorabilia of which writer who lived there from 1898 to 1916?

c Which writer lived at Monk's House, Rodmell, near Lewes, for many years until 1941?

11 YOUR STARTER FOR

The holder of which honorary title in the House of Commons has only one duty, which is to preside over the election of a new speaker?

Seas

a Which sea is named after the sixteenth-century Dutch explorer and navigator who died during his third voyage of exploration in 1596?

b Which sea was named after the British Rear Admiral and Polar explorer who charted it in 1841?

c Which sea was named after the Danish navigator who joined the fleet of Tsar Peter The Great who, in 1724 appointed him leader of an expedition to determine whether Asia and North America were connected by land?

12 YOUR STARTER FOR

Which painting by William Holman Hunt shows the figure of Jesus bearing a lantern on a moonlit night knocking on the door of a house?

Novels

a Whose novel, first published in 1993, told of Lata and her mother's search to find a husband, the 'suitable boy' of its title?

b In the novel by Timothy Mo, shortlisted for the Booker Prize in 1986, which territory was the 'Insular Possession' of the title?

c In which Booker Prize-winning novel by a Japanese-born writer does an elderly English butler come to the conclusion that his master, Lord Darlington, had been a Nazi sympathizer?

13 YOUR STARTER FOR

Which military corps was formally organized by the Emperor Augustus in about 27 BC and disbanded by Constantine in AD 312?

Geochronology

a Which is the first era of Earth's history comprising almost 90 per cent of geological time?

b During which geological period, the youngest of the Mesozoic era, did the dinosaurs suddenly disappear?

c Also referred to as the recent, which epoch is the latest of geological time, covering approximately the last 10 000 years of the Earth's history?

14 **YOUR STARTER FOR**

In which film did another diner say, 'I'll have what she's having' on seeing Meg Ryan's 'orgasm' in a restaurant?

 Dance

a In which Cornish town is the 'Furry Dance' performed each May?

b Which American dancer caused a sensation when she first performed in *La Revue Nègre* in Paris in 1925?

c Which occasional dancer was the daughter of Herod Philip and Herodias and stepdaughter of Herod Antipas?

15 **YOUR STARTER FOR**

What is involved in the crime of embracery?

 Swans

a Celebrated in legend, and immortalized in opera, who was the 'The Swan Knight'?

b Which classical Greek writer was known as 'The Swan of Meander'?

c Who first described Shakespeare as 'The Swan of Avon'?

16 **YOUR STARTER FOR**

Which country played in 17 unsuccessful World Cup Final matches between 1962 and 1994 before finally beating Greece 1 – 0 in the 1994 tournament, going on to beat Germany in the quarter finals and finally losing 2 – 1 to Italy in the semi-finals?

 American presidents

a Of the first five American presidents, four were born in which state?

b Ronald Reagan is the oldest man to have been inaugurated as president of the United States. Who is the second oldest, dying in office in 1841?

c Who has been the longest serving American president, holding office for more than 12 years?

17 **YOUR STARTER FOR**

Ninian, Cormorant, Thistle and Brent are all what?

Heraldry

a In heraldry, what is meant if an animal is shown gardant?

b What would it mean if an animal was displayed trippant?

c What is meant by the heraldic term marshalling?

18 **YOUR STARTER FOR**

With which band did jazz virtuoso John Coltrane come to prominence between 1955 and 1960 before founding his own group?

Trains

a What was the name of the last steam engine to be built for service on British railways in 1960?

b Which corporation, partly financed by the federal government, took over the operation of almost all American intercity passenger trains in 1971?

c In which country in 1988 did trains begin operating through the 33½ mile long, undersea tunnel known as the Seikan tunnel?

19 **YOUR STARTER FOR**

Which famous work of Persian literature was translated into English by Edward Fitzgerald in 1859?

Film roles

a Which ancient historical figure was portrayed on film by Fritz Leiber in 1917 and subsequently by many actors, including Claude Rains, Rex Harrison, John Gielgud and Kenneth Williams?

b Which fictional character was played by Forest Holger-Madsen in a series of Danish films made in 1908? Actors who later played the role included Basil Rathbone, Peter Cushing, Christopher Lee and Christopher Plummer.

c Which monarch has been portrayed on screen by Richard Burton, Charles Laughton and Sid James?

20 **YOUR STARTER FOR**

What term is used for a uniformly wound coil of wire in the form of a cylinder, having a length much greater than its diameter and producing a uniform magnetic field along its axis when a current is passed through it?

BONUS QUESTIONS

Weddings

a Who danced beneath the moon on their wedding night after purchasing a wedding ring for a shilling?

b Which wealthy merchant, who was Lord Mayor of London in 1397, 1406 and 1419, married Alice Fitzwaryn, daughter of a West Country landowner?

c Who were married by the Reverend Robert Jardine on 3 June 1937?

SPARE STARTER QUESTIONS

21 Founded by John Christie in 1934 at his Sussex home, which festival of opera is held every summer?

22 What word describes an official publication dealing with the doses, preparations, sources and tests of recognized drugs?

23 What was the name of the oil tanker that ran aground on 24 March 1989 on Bligh Reef in Prince William Sound, Alaska, causing widespread pollution?

24 The computer programming language LISP derives its name from the combination of which two words?

25 To which court are Ambassadors from abroad formally accredited, although new Ambassadors present their credentials to the Queen at Buckingham Palace?

Game seven

1

YOUR STARTER FOR

What number is produced when silver, ruby and golden are added together?

Maps

a What, originated as 'dissected maps', were devised to teach geography in eighteenth-century England?

b 'Roll up that map; it will not be wanted these ten years.' These were William Pitt's words, referring to the map of Europe, after hearing the news of which battle of 1805?

c Complete the final line of the following verse by Edmund Clerihew Bentley:
'The art of biography
Is different from geography.
Geography is about maps,
But...'.

2

YOUR STARTER FOR

Where collectively will you find W. M. Baker, Winfred Norbury, G. R. Sinclair and the composer's wife Caroline Alice?

Children's television

a Which cartoon feline's gang consisted of Benny the Ball, Brains, Choo-Choo, Spook and Fancy, while his hapless opponent was Officer Dibble?

b Which of the 'Wacky Racers' rode in the Compact Pussycat?

c Who was regularly rescued from the clutches of his arch foe Cutthroat Jake by the *Black Pig*'s cabin boy, Tom?

3

YOUR STARTER FOR

Which term was applied to the architectural style of Wright, Gropius, Loos and Hoffman by Hitchcock and Johnson in their influential 1932 book?

Former London landmarks

a Which building, originally sited in Hyde Park, was later dismantled and re-erected in a park in Sydenham where it was destroyed by fire in 1936?

b Which building was demolished in 1902, the Central Criminal Courts, or Old Bailey, being constructed on the site and formally opened five years later in 1907 by King Edward VII?

c Which structure, the historic western entrance to the city of London situated at the end of Fleet Street, was dismantled in 1878 and moved to Theobolds Park in Hertfordshire?

4

YOUR STARTER FOR

If every batsman in a cricket team is bowled first ball, what will be the number of the only batsman shown as 'not out' at the end of the innings?

Very dead languages

a Deciphered in 1952 by Michael Ventris, by what name is the syllabic script, used for writing the form of the Greek language known as Mycenaean Greek from about 1400 until about 1150 BC, known?

b Which language, spoken by early neighbours of the Romans, does not seem to have been an Indo-European language and still defies translation?

c Which extinct East Germanic language is the earliest recorded Germanic language?

5

YOUR STARTER FOR

Which plant, cultivated in many varieties for its large, edible leaves, derives its name from the Latin for 'of milk', because of the milky liquid it can exude when cut?

Recipients of the Order of Merit

a In 1907, who became the first woman to receive the Order of Merit?

b Which British dramatist and novelist was created a baronet in 1913 and awarded the Order of Merit nine years later?

c Which American-born writer was awarded the Order of Merit and the Nobel Prize for Literature in 1948?

6 YOUR STARTER FOR

In August 1993, Salman Rushdie made a surprise stage appearance at Wembley during a concert by which group?

Preventative medicine

a The first vaccine was introduced by Dr Edward Jenner in 1798, when he noted that the introduction of which virus offered protection against smallpox?

b The BCG vaccine protects against which disease?

c Which Polish-American physician and microbiologist developed the oral vaccine against poliomyelitis approved for use in 1960?

7 YOUR STARTER FOR

Which king described smoking as 'loathsome to the eye, hateful to the nose, harmful to the brain, dangerous to the lungs...' in his *A Counterblast To Tobacco,* written in 1604?

Musical partnerships

a In 1928, which composer collaborated with Bertolt Brecht in transposing John Gay's *The Beggar's Opera* to the Berlin underworld?

b Who was the lyricist for Leonard Bernstein's *West Side Story*?

c Which songwriting team had their work celebrated by the 1991 tribute album *Two Rooms*?

8 YOUR STARTER FOR

The Court of the Stannaries of Cornwall and Devon, whose powers were abolished in 1897, has jurisdiction for the administration of justice among which group of people?

Land

a In the Bible, who, according to Acts, purchased a plot of land known as Potter's Field?

b What name is given to the sale of their North American territories by the French Government in 1803?

c Who owns the Oval cricket ground, home of Surrey County Cricket Club?

9 YOUR STARTER FOR

What happened politically in Britain in February and October 1974 that had not occurred twice in the same year since 1910?

Codenames or coded messages

a In 1924, the architect Giles Gilbert Scott won a national competition with a design codenamed K2. What was K2?

b What was the coded message reputedly sent by Sir Charles Napier to Lord Ellenborough in 1843 informing him that the Indian Province of Sindh had been taken?

c Which ill-fated Second World War enterprise was codenamed Operation Valkyrie?

10

YOUR STARTER FOR

Which broadcaster, who, between 1972 and 1982, was television critic for *The Observer*, has written a series of autobiographies, the first of which, *Unreliable Memoirs*, was published in 1980?

Exiles

a In May 1994, the former First Secretary of the East German Communist Party, Erich Honecker, died in exile. In which country?

b Who lived in exile for 20 years before returning home in 1680 as John Clarke?

c The deposed Shah of Iran died in exile in 1980. In which country?

11

YOUR STARTER FOR 10

What appears as a 'concentric arc, with a common centre on the line connecting the eye of the observer with the light source'? Sometimes two appear together and its outer border is normally red.

French dramatists

a What is the name of the French dramatist, considered the creator of French classical tragedy, whose best-known play, *Le Cid*, was suppressed by Richelieu, supposedly for not observing the dramatic unities?

b Which French tragic dramatist ceased to write for the theatre after the success of *Phaedre* in 1677, until Madame de Maintenon, the second wife of Louis XIV, commissioned his last two plays for her school for the daughters of impoverished nobles at Saint-Cyr?

c Which French dramatist collapsed on stage during an early performance of his play *Le Malade Imaginaire* in 1673, dying later the same night?

12 **YOUR STARTER FOR**
Which two Latin words contain an instruction to 'Enjoy the present' or literally 'Seize the day'?

Sporting firsts

a What were worn in an FA Cup Final for the first time in 1933?

b What made their first appearance on a British racecourse at Newmarket in July 1965?

c What was first introduced into high jumping by the gold medallist at the 1968 Mexico Olympics?

13 **YOUR STARTER FOR**
The Danish philosopher Søren Kierkegaard was one of the seminal figures of which group of philosophies whose proponents include Nicola Abagnano, Martin Heidegger and Jean Paul Sartre?

Burial places of English monarchs

a In which English cathedral is King John entombed?

b Gloucester Cathedral contains the tomb of which English King, murdered at Berkeley Castle in 1327?

c After his execution in 1649, King Charles I was entombed in which castle?

14 **YOUR STARTER FOR**
If Number 31 is Paris and Number 36 is Linz, which city is Number 38?

Famous speeches

a Supply the next seven words in the American orator Patrick Henry's speech at the second Virginia Convention of 1775: 'I know not what course others may take; but as for me...'?

b What were the next five words of Harold Macmillan at a 1957 Conservative rally when he said: 'Let us be frank about it. Most of our people have...'?

c In her Guildhall speech of November 1992, which two words did the Queen use to describe her year?

15 **YOUR STARTER FOR**
Food additives approved by the European Union are given E numbers. What function is performed by additives numbered from 100 to 199?

Islands

a Which group of islands were known as the Fortunate Islands in ancient times?

b Off the coast of which country is Devil's Island, the former penal colony?

c On which island did the *Bounty* mutineers under Fletcher Christian settle after the famous mutiny?

16 YOUR STARTER FOR

Which 1932 novel took its title from the words spoken by Miranda in the last act of *The Tempest*?

 Mathematicians

a Which English mathematician, who helped establish modern symbolic logic and whose algebra of logic is fundamental to the design of digital computer circuits, fully stated his ideas in *Laws of Thought*, published in 1854?

b Born in Brunn in Austria-Hungary in 1906, who is the author of the proof which states that within any rigidly logical mathematical system, there are propositions or questions that cannot be proved or disproved by the axioms of that system and that, therefore, it is uncertain that the basic axioms of arithmetic will not give rise to contradictions – a proof that has wide repercussions in twentieth-century mathematics?

c The papers of which English mathematician and logician, who, in 1948, became Deputy Director of the computing laboratory at Manchester University, are widely acknowledged as the foundation of research in artificial intelligence?

17 YOUR STARTER FOR

Which internationally renowned university, founded in 1636, was named in honour of the puritan minister who bequeathed his library and half of his estate to the university?

 Japanese culture

a What name is given to the popular Japanese entertainment whose three characters signify 'song', 'dance' and 'acting' or 'skill'?

b Chado, Cha-No-Yu (cha-no-yoo) and Wabi, rooted in the principle of Zen Buddhism and introduced to Japan from China, are highly sophisticated ceremonies for the drinking of what?

c What name is given to the Japanese poetic form, consisting of 17 syllables, arranged in 3 lines of 5, 7 and 5 syllables each?

18

YOUR STARTER FOR 10

What did Captain Charles Yeager do with Glamorous Glennis in October 1947?

British politics

a Which politician resigned on 1 November 1990, stating in his resignation letter, 'I do not believe that I can any longer serve with honour as a member of your Government'?

b Who was elected leader of the Scottish Nationalist Party in September 1990?

c Who resigned his post as Employment Secretary in January 1990 to devote more time to his family?

19

YOUR STARTER FOR 10

According to John Betjeman, which Berkshire town 'isn't fit for humans now'?

Brothers

a The brothers Thomas and Henry Pelham were the only pair of British brothers to hold which office?

b Henry VIII's widow, Catherine Parr, married the brother of one of Henry's earlier wives. Who was he?

c Which cabinet post did Robert Kennedy hold in his brother John's administration?

20

YOUR STARTER FOR 10

Devised as a means of postponing the date appointed for her own execution, the collection of tales recounted to her husband, Schariah, by the narrator Scheherazade over a nominal period of 1001 nights is generally known by which title?

Saints

a Who was the child martyr, executed during the Diocletian persecution in 304, his name being associated by most people with a Gilbert Scott building in Euston Road?

b Which famous battle was fought on St Crispin's Day, 25 October?

c With which saint would you associate the best-known work of the American W. C. Handy?

SPARE STARTER QUESTIONS

21 What name is given to the microscopic thread-like part of a cell that carries hereditary information in the form of genes?

22 In 1994, which planet was furthest from the Sun and will remain so until March 1999 when it will again be Pluto that is furthest from the sun?

23 What word, derived from the Spanish for 'saw', prefixes the name of mountain ranges such as Madre in Mexico and Nevada in the United States and Spain?

24 Which literary heroine had an unsatisfying affair with a successful playwright called Michaelis before her better-known relationship with one of her husband's servants?

25 What begins as an alevin, moves to a parr or a pink; then becomes a smolt and a grilse. If it returns to the sea after breeding time, it is often in poor condition, and then called a kelt?

Game eight

1

What name is given to the Egyptian Christians, numbering about one million, who claim they received the gospel from St Mark, the first Bishop of Alexandria?

Artists
a According to legend, which artist drew a perfect circle as an example of his work, in order to secure a papal commission?
b Which artist was knighted by Charles I and made court painter in 1632?
c Which artist was forced to flee Rome in 1606 after murdering a tennis opponent?

2
YOUR STARTER FOR 10
Deriving its name from the stream near Stirling where it was fought, which battle of 1314 marked the defeat of Edward II's English army by the Scots under Robert The Bruce?

Australian prime ministers
a Which Australian Prime Minister, who succeeded Robert Menzies, relaxed immigration and citizenship laws and supported involvement in the Vietnam war until his death in 1967, apparently by drowning?
b Which Australian became his country's Labour Prime Minister in 1972 but had a troubled administration and was finally dismissed by the Governor-General, Sir John Kerr, on 11 November 1975?
c Who did Paul Keating replace as Australia's Prime Minister in December 1991?

3
YOUR STARTER FOR 10
What term, deriving from a ballad by Henry Woodfall, first published in 1735, is used for an elderly couple living in marital harmony?

Chemistry
a What, in 1887, did Swedish chemist Arrhenius define as substances that dissociate in water to yield ions, of which positive ions are hydrogen ions?

b Which measure of the acidity of a solution is defined as log-to-the-base-10 of 1 over the hydrogen ion concentration?

c What name is given to a solution, usually containing a weak acid and its salt, that tends to maintain its pH value and resists changes that might be caused by addition of hydrogen or hydroxide ions?

4 YOUR STARTER FOR

In Greek mythology, which Titan, the son of Uranus, fathered the dawn, the sun and the moon?

English theatres

a Which is the third playhouse making up the National Theatre along with the Olivier and the Lyttleton?

b In the early 1960s, which London theatre became the first temporary home of the National Theatre Company?

c In 1973, when Laurence Olivier resigned as the National Theatre's Director owing to ill-health, who replaced him?

5 YOUR STARTER FOR

Which British architect, who was awarded a knighthood 12 days before his death in 1992, designed the Neue Staatsgalerie in Stuttgart?

Flags

a On the flag of which European country will you see an armillary sphere, an early navigation instrument?

b Which Asiatic country's flag includes the ancient Chinese Yin-Yang symbol, which represents all the opposites that occur in Nature?

c Which country's flag contains a representation of the Buddhist Charkra symbol, which represents peaceful change?

6 YOUR STARTER FOR

Which branch of mechanics deals with the behaviour of bodies under the action of forces that produce changes in their motion?

Ruins

a In which ancient city are the remains of the Imperial Palace of Xerxes, which was destroyed about 330 BC by the army of Alexander the Great?

b Only a small portion of the Great Temple of Solomon in Jerusalem remains. By what name is this fragment known?

c Originally, 12 were constructed by Edward I to commemorate his first wife, but only 3 remain. They are at Waltham, Northampton and Geddington. What are they?

7 **YOUR STARTER FOR**
To the nearest whole number, what is the sum of pi, the ratio of the circumference of a circle to its diameter and E, the base of natural logarithms?

Professions
a According to the first word engraved after his name on his tombstone, what was the profession of Benjamin Franklin?
b What was the profession of Thomas Guy, the founder of Guy's Hospital?
c Appointed Professor of Chemistry at the Medico-Surgical Academy in St Petersburg in 1864, he is now best remembered in an entirely different field. Who was he?

8 **YOUR STARTER FOR**
Which organization was founded in 1953 by the Reverend Chad Varah?

Deaths in myth and legend
a According to one version of the legend, which youth, loved by Apollo, was killed when the jealous Zephyrus diverted a discus thrown by Apollo to hit him?
b Acis, a shepherd who was killed by his jealous rival Polyphemus, loved which sea-nymph?
c What was the ultimate fate of the huntsman Actaeon, turned into a stag by Artemis after he inadvertently saw her bathing?

9 **YOUR STARTER FOR**
What is the more familiar name of Gravelly (Grave-ly) Hill Interchange, junction 6 on the M6 motorway, just north of Birmingham?

Fridges
a Which American businessman and inventor, who lived from 1886 to1956, is best known for developing a process for freezing food in small packages suitable for retailing?
b Refrigerants are known by three-digit numbers, reflecting their molecular constitution; the first digit is the number of carbon atoms minus one in the refrigerant molecule, the second digit is the number

of hydrogen atoms plus one. The number of atoms of which element is represented by the third digit?

c Which element, present in CFCs, is missing from the new environmentally friendly refrigerants that are replacing the CFCs?

10 YOUR STARTER FOR 10

In July 1798, which English poet was inspired to compose one of his works while standing above the ruins of an abbey on the banks of the River Wye in what is now the county of Gwent?

French history

a What name is given to the series of uprisings that took place in France between 1648 and 1653, which ended in a clear victory for Mazarin and was the last challenge to the Monarchy until 1789?

b Known from 1789 until 1792 as the Society of the Friends of the Constitution, what was the popular name for the extreme revolutionary group that ruled France from mid 1793 until mid 1794, and so-called because they met in a former Dominican convent?

c What name did the Parisian radicals who rebelled against the Government in 1871 after the Franco-Prussian War, give themselves, in emulation of the Jacobins of the French Revolution?

11 YOUR STARTER FOR 10

Which television detective made his first appearance in 1981 and worked for the Bureau des Etrangers?

Bears

a Which bear, the largest living land carnivore, takes its name from an island in the Gulf of Alaska, which is its natural habitat?

b Which bear, whose scientific name is *Ursus maritimus*, has been protected since 1973 by an international agreement that allowed it to be hunted only by local populations using traditional weapons?

c Who described himself as '...a bear of very little brain...'?

12 YOUR STARTER FOR 10

What is the plural of kibbutz?

Editions of the Bible

a Why is the sixteenth-century Geneva Bible often given the nickname the Breeches Bible?

b Which version of the Bible first appeared in 1611?

c A publication of the Bible completed in 1976 and called 'Today's English Version' is popularly known by which American title?

13 YOUR STARTER FOR 10

Where could you find male members of the *Cervidae* family mingling freely with *Ursidae* in central London between Monday morning and Friday evening?

Musical firsts

a Benjamin Britten's *War Requiem* was first performed in 1962 at the consecration of which cathedral, linked by a canopy to the old, bombed building?

b Which Verdi opera, first performed at La Scala in 1893, was based on Shakespeare's play *The Merry Wives of Windsor*?

c Which oratorio was first performed in Dublin in 1742 and established a tradition the following year when King George II, followed by the entire assembly, rose to his feet as the chorus that closes part 2 was performed?

14 YOUR STARTER FOR 10

What unit, named after a French inventor who patented a telegraph code based on sets of binary digits to replace Morse code, measures the rate at which information can be transmitted, for example, between computers?

Poetical epithets

a Which poet, the bicentenary of whose birth was celebrated in 1993, was known as the Northamptonshire poet?

b Which epithet was applied to the Scottish poet James Hogg?

c Which early eighteenth-century satirical poet and essayist was known as 'The Wasp of Twickenham'?

15 YOUR STARTER FOR 10

When John Major announced his first cabinet in November 1990, what was absent for the first time since 1965?

Capital cities

a Which European capital city was known as Christiana from 1624 to 1925 after King Christian IV?

b Which administrative capital city was founded in 1855 by the son of the Dutch settler from whom the city took its name?

c Which capital city, founded in 1541, was named in honour of a patron saint of Spain?

16 YOUR STARTER FOR

In printing, what term describes a style of Roman letter stripped of embellishments, such as the baseline on which lower-case n, m and l rest?

Military leaders

a Which South American soldier and statesman, who was born in Caracas in 1783, is known as 'El Libertador'?

b Which military leader, of Spanish-Irish descent, who led the Chilean forces to independence from Spain, became its first head of state in 1817?

c The name of which military leader in the Argentine war for independence, who died in 1820, is now best remembered by an incident that happened 162 years after his death?

17 YOUR STARTER FOR

Who said, as he took his first steps on his native soil for 20 years, 'I know that I am returning to a Russia tortured, stunned, altered beyond recognition, convulsively searching for itself, for its own true identity'?

Numbers

a What name is given to the product of all positive integers less than or equal to a given number and denoted by that number and an exclamation mark?

b What name, from the Latin for 'deaf', is applied to an irrational number, especially one that can be written as the root of a rational number?

c What name for 10 to the power 100 was coined by the nine-year-old nephew of American mathematician Dr Edward Kasner?

18 YOUR STARTER FOR

Lucy can now be seen in the House of Commons, where she succeeded Offa in 1994. Who is Lucy?

People with the same surname

a Name the father and son who received Academy Awards for Best Supporting Actor and Best Director respectively for a 1947 film.

b The English writer of the novel *The Good Soldier*, published in 1915, shared which two forenames with his grandfather, a nineteenth-century painter associated with the Pre-Raphaelite Brotherhood?

c Give the Christian names of the following two people who shared the same surname: a nineteenth-century English actor who revived popular interest in Shakespeare and an American writer who used the pseudonyms Geoffrey Crayon and Diedrich Knickerbocker?

19 YOUR STARTER FOR

During the Renaissance period, children in some Italian orphanages were often given musical instruction at State expense. The Italian term for this practice has given rise to which word, describing an institution for education in musical performances and composition?

BONUS QUESTIONS

Fountains

a Who composed the orchestral piece 'Fountains of Rome'?

b Which sculptor's major works include the Triton Fountain in the Piazza Barberini and the Fountain of the Four Rivers in the Piazza Navona, both in Rome?

c If you want to return to Rome, according to legend, into which fountain should you toss a coin in order for your wish to be granted?

20 YOUR STARTER FOR

Sir Peter Teazle did it in 1787, Cardinal Beaufort did it in 1805, as did Captain Cuttle in 1922. It usually takes just over two and a half minutes to do. What is it?

BONUS QUESTIONS

Pseudonyms

a Who used the pseudonym Ralph Robinson for articles he contributed to *Annals of Agriculture*?

b Queen Anne corresponded with Sarah Churchill using the name Mrs Morley. What name did the Duchess use in their correspondence?

c Who used the pseudonym Richard Saunders for the articles he contributed to *Poor Richard's Almanac*?

SPARE STARTER QUESTIONS

21 Which element, the last in the periodic table to have a stable, non-radioactive isotope, has relative atomic mass of 208.98, proton number 83 and chemical symbol 'BI'?

22 Which state of north-west India, in the Himalayan foothills, has a name meaning 'five rivers'?

23 Who, despite failing his finals at Oxford in 1880, was appointed Professor of Latin at Cambridge in 1911?

24 'Dead Belgians don't count' was the original title for which Channel Four comedy series, set in a newsroom?

25 Fragments of the comet Shoemaker Levy 9 hit which major planet during July 1994?

Game nine

1

YOUR STARTER FOR

Which former Junior Defence Minister's admission that he had been 'economical with the actualité' led to the collapse of the Matrix-Churchill trial in November 1992?

Châteaux

a Empress Josephine died in 1814 at which château about five miles west of Paris?

b The Renaissance Château Chambord, begun by Francis I after his return from Italy in 1519, is the largest in which valley?

c *Le Château de ma Mère* was written by which French author and film maker who died in 1974?

2

YOUR STARTER FOR

Which East African country contains the Tarangire National Park, the Ngorongoro Crater Game Reserve and the Serengeti National Park?

Codes and code breaking

a Which literary work, written in a form of shorthand known as tachygraphy, was deciphered by John Smith in 1825 over 120 years after the writer's death, of which about a quarter was published, after editing by Lord Braybrooke, with an unexpurgated edition finally being published between 1970 and 1983?

b The decipherment of inscriptions on what, begun by Thomas Young and completed by Jean-François Champollion, led to the understanding of hieroglyphic writing?

c Which writer of children's stories began keeping a journal in code at the age of 15, which was deciphered by Leslie Linder, an untiring enthusiast of her writings, and published in 1966, 23 years after her death in her beloved Lake District?

3

YOUR STARTER FOR

What is the popular name for impure corundum or aluminium oxide, much used as an abrasive agent?

American states

a Which American state is bordered by Nebraska to the north, Colorado to the west and Missouri to the east?

b The state of Maine borders only one other American state – which one?

c With which state does Texas share her shortest state boundary?

4

YOUR STARTER FOR

The numbers 2¹/₂ and 33¹/₃ are sequels to which film starring Leslie Nielsen and Priscilla Presley?

The Sun

a By what process is the energy radiated by the Sun produced?

b What name is given to the visible, luminous surface of the Sun?

c To the nearest minute, how long does it take light from the Sun to reach the Earth?

5

YOUR STARTER FOR

In the phonetic alphabet, used in radio communication, where 'A' is alpha and 'B' is bravo, which word represents the letter 'R'?

Classical singers

a Elgar's 'Sea Pictures' were especially composed for which English contralto who made her singing début in 1892?

b Benjamin Britten wrote the title roles of Peter Grimes and Albert Herring and the part of Captain Vere in *Billy Budd* for which English tenor?

c In 1959, Covent Garden produced a special revival of Donizetti's *Lucia di Lammermoor* for which Australian soprano?

6

YOUR STARTER FOR

Published in 1994, *The Hippopotamus* is which actor and comedian's second novel?

Aviation feats

a In July 1981, the solar-powered aircraft Solar Challenger became the first of its type to achieve what?

b What was historic about the Channel crossing by the aircraft Gossamer Albatross piloted by Bryan Allen in June 1979?

c What was unique about the circumnavigation of the globe made by the aircraft Voyager in December 1986?

7

YOUR STARTER FOR 10

Which muscular, membranous sac is pear-shaped and expandable and, in humans, is situated on the underside of the liver?

BONUS QUESTIONS

Artists' names

a The seventeenth-century French artist Claude Gellée is better known by the name he adopted throughout his professional life, which was derived from the province of his birth. Who was he?

b Which Italian artist, the subject of a 1986 Derek Jarman film, was born in 1573, baptized Michelangelo Merisi, but adopted the name of his home town as his professional name?

c Jacopo Robusti's professional name was derived from the occupation of his father, a dyer. Who was Robusti?

8

YOUR STARTER FOR 10

Which two states were the protagonists in the Seven Weeks' War of 1866?

BONUS QUESTIONS

Glasses

a Bumping glasses were popular in the eighteenth century. Why were they so called?

b Whose celebrated couplet made a statement (probably erroneous) about 'girls who wear glasses'?

c *Glass's Guide* is a guide to the price of what?

9

YOUR STARTER FOR 10

Which small, everyday utensil was known in England as early as the ninth century, though it was not used at table until about the last quarter of the seventeenth century?

BONUS QUESTIONS

Trials and prisons

a Who was sentenced to death for treason in 1603, but, after being reprieved, was imprisoned in the tower until 1616, finally being executed in 1618 after offending Spain in an unsuccessful search for gold?

b Who was sentenced to three years' penal servitude in 1913 for incitement to violence after the Women's Social and Political Union (WSPU) had bombed Lloyd George's home?

c Tennessee high school teacher John Scopes was convicted and fined $100 in 1925 for violating State law by teaching which theory?

10

YOUR STARTER FOR

Advection and radiation are two of the types of which meteorological phenomenon that occurs when atmospheric water vapour is cooled to the dew point and condenses on condensation nuclei, causing horizontal visibility to be reduced below 1 kilometre?

Books about Margaret, now Baroness, Thatcher

a What is the title of Margaret Thatcher's memoirs, published in 1993?

b A 1989 publication about Margaret Thatcher, entitled *One of Us*, and *The Thatcher Phenomenon* from 1986 were written by which British journalist?

c 1990 saw the publication of a book by former columnist at *The Times* Geoffrey Smith that looked at the 'special relationship' between Margaret Thatcher and whom?

11

YOUR STARTER FOR

Designed by William Railton, put up between 1839 and 1842, and topped by a 17-foot tall statue by E. H. Baily, what is the name of this memorial in Trafalgar Square?

Plants

a What name is given to the growth of plant organs in response to gravity such that a main stem grows upwards and a main root grows downwards, irrespective of the positions in which they were placed?

b The part of the plant embryo that develops into the shoot system is known as the plumule. What name is given to the part of the plant embryo that develops into the root system?

c What name is given to a horizontal underground plant stem enabling the plant to survive from one growing season to the next and capable of producing the shoot and root systems of a new plant?

12

YOUR STARTER FOR

What was founded in 1865 to oppose reconstruction after the American Civil War and led the Government to pass acts against it in 1871? It re-emerged in 1915 in Atlanta, Georgia, but, since the early 1980s, membership has dwindled.

The Apocalypse

a By what name is the New Testament Book, Apocalypse of John, also known?

b The film *Apocalypse Now* was based on the plot of which novel?

c Which Spanish author wrote *The Four Horsemen of the Apocalypse*, which dealt with the First World War?

13 YOUR STARTER FOR
By what name is bovine spongiform encephalopathy, or BSE, commonly known?

Uncles and nephews
a Which nephew of Henry I – the son of his sister, Adela – reigned from 1135 to 1154?
b Killed by Basques in 778, which Paladin – a hero of medieval romances – was, according to legend, a nephew of the Frankish King, Charlemagne?
c Who was the nephew of Napoleon I, elected as President in 1851 before assuming the title of Emperor?

14 YOUR STARTER FOR
Which novel features the words 'All animals are equal but some animals are more equal than others'?

Deaths of operatic heroines
a Who joins her lover, who has been condemned to be buried alive, to die with him?
b Who leaps from the battlements of the Castel Sant'Angelo after seeing her lover's death by firing squad?
c Who comes to London as a prostitute, where she is killed by Jack the Ripper?

15 YOUR STARTER FOR
The first four notes of which of Beethoven's symphonies were used in BBC broadcasts to occupied Europe during the Second World War?

Royal last words
a The last words of which English monarch (who was succeeded by her distant cousin) are said to have been, 'All my possessions for a moment of time!'?
b Which British monarch, who converted to Catholicism on his deathbed, is said to have asked to be excused for being 'a most unconscionable time dying'?
c Which English monarch's last words are reputed to have been, 'All is lost! Monks, monks, monks'?

16 YOUR STARTER FOR

Which impressionist artist painted over 30 studies of the Thames during several visits to London at the turn of the century?

Coasts

a What name is given to the south-east coast of India, from Point Calimire in the south to the mouth of the Krishna river in the north, said to be in an Edward Lear poem the home of the Yonghy-Bonghy-Bo?

b What name was given to the coast of North Africa, notorious for the Muslim pirates who operated from there?

c Centred on the resort of Porto Cervo, the Costa Smeralda, or Emerald Coast, is found to the north east of which Mediterranean island?

17 YOUR STARTER FOR

What was the common factor in the accession to the English throne of the following Kings: Henry I, John, James II, William IV, George VI?

Verse

a Which ancient verse form consists of four dactyls or spondees, then an invariable dactyl and spondee, divided usually in the third foot by a caesura?

b Who introduced the sonnet into English, copying the Petrarchan style, which has since been used by every major English poet?

c What name is given to verse without rhyme, especially the iambic pentameter, first used by Henry Howard, Earl of Surrey, in his translation of the *Aeneid*, which was published in 1557?

18 YOUR STARTER FOR

The Kerch Strait connects the Sea of Azov with which much larger sea?

Clubs

a Which saxophonist opened his world-renowned jazz club in London in 1959?

b Which club was founded in 1787 by a group of noblemen headed by the Earl of Winchelsea?

c Which fictional club, first appearing in print in April 1836, was formed to enable its members to report on their 'journeys and adventures, and observations of characters and manners'?

19 YOUR STARTER FOR

The flickering light supposedly produced by the spontaneous combustion of marsh gas and commonly called will-o'-the-wisp or jack-o'-lantern is more properly known by which Latin name?

Treasure

a In England and Wales, which official decides whether or not property found is treasure trove and whether or not the finder has good title to the goods?

b Whose treasure, including the bejewelled sword of Tristram, was lost between Cross Keys and Long Sutton in the thirteenth century?

c By what name is the group of late Roman silver vessels known, which were found in Suffolk in 1942, and now housed in the British Museum?

20 YOUR STARTER FOR

Which West Indian all-rounder, while playing for Nottinghamshire in 1968, became the first player in first-class cricket to score 36 runs from a 6-ball over?

Dictionaries and their compilers

a *The Devil's Dictionary,* published in 1906 and famed for its sardonic definitions, is the work of which American journalist and humorist, said to have disappeared in Mexico during the Revolution of Pancho Villa?

b Which English writer defined lexicographer as 'a writer of dictionaries, a harmless drudge', in his own dictionary, the compilation of which occupied him from 1747 to 1755?

c Which two German-born brothers who are now best remembered for their work in an entirely different field of writing, began the *Deutsches Wörterbuch,* a large, German dictionary, in the early nineteenth century?

SPARE STARTER QUESTIONS

21 Which French explorer was the first European to explore the St Lawrence river to its navigable height, the bridge across the river in Montreal being named after him?

22 *The Emerald City* was the title of the first draft of which novel, published in 1900 and made into a classic film starring Judy Garland as the heroine Dorothy Gale?

23 In art, what word refers to a sketch that an artist uses as a guide for a painting or other work, although in another context it can also describe a finished drawing or series of drawings?

24 What word, coming from the Greek 'to excite' is applied to chemical substances produced by one group of cells in the body that exert an effect on another group of cells which may be in a part of the body distant from the cells producing the substance?

25 Which event, that took place on 15 June 1215, is surprisingly omitted from Shakespeare's *The Life and Death of King John*?

Game ten

I

YOUR STARTER FOR

The science of ekistics involves which broad field of study?

Shakespearean nativities

a Which Scot 'was from his mother's womb/untimely ripp'd'?

b Who was sent before his time 'into this breathing world scarce half made up'?

c Who was born 'on lammas-eve, at night'?

2

YOUR STARTER FOR

Which poet bought a house near Freshwater, Isle of Wight, with the proceeds from *Maud*, his favourite walk along the Downs to the Needles later being named after him?

Battle sites

a What alternative name was given to the American Civil War battle of 1863, fought on and around the summit of Lookout Mountain?

b In 1627, Charles I sent the Duke of Buckingham on an abortive attempt to help French Huguenots defend which city?

c *The Ballad of Chevy Chase* is an account of which battle, at which Hotspur was defeated in 1388?

3

YOUR STARTER FOR

Whose 'adieux' marked the departure of Archduke Rudolph from Vienna after Napoleon's arrival in that city – his absence – and his return?

Suicides

a In 1920, Jeanne Hebuterne committed suicide the day after the death of her artist lover. Who was he?

b In 1967, Kenneth Halliwell committed suicide after murdering his lover in their London flat. Who was his lover?

c Which famous sportsman took his own life in 1886 when he was 29 years old?

4

YOUR STARTER FOR

Due to return to Chinese rule in December 1999, which territory, covering an area of some 16 square kilometres with an estimated population of about 400 000, comprises a small, narrow peninsula of land which projects from the Chinese mainland province of Guangdong?

Names of new European Rebulics

a Which new European republic's name in its own language is Hrvatska (hur-vatska)?

b Which republic's name in its own language is Lietuva (li-etoova)?

c By what name is the republic, which previously had used to be known as Belorussia (byellorusha) in the days of the Soviet Union, now know?

5

YOUR STARTER FOR

Also known as China clay, which natural aluminium silicate is administered orally with morphine in cases of diarrhoea and food poisoning?

Sacred places in India

a The Sikh Golden Temple, the site of which was donated by the Mogul Emperor Akbar in 1577, is in which city of the Punjab?

b Which building at Agra in Uttar Pradesh was built of white marble in the seventeenth century as a tomb for Shah Jahan's favourite wife?

c Which rock caves in India's Maharashtra state include the Great Temple of Kailasa?

6

YOUR STARTER FOR

Believed by experts to have originated more than 500 years ago and often referred to as the 'Royal dog of the Americas', what is the name of the smallest breed of dog?

The human body

a Which acid is derived from the breakdown of glycogen and is produced in the body during muscular activity?

b A person suffering from parosmia has their sense of smell affected in what way?

c Which two ligaments, so attached as to become taut when the limb is straightened, are located in the interior of the knee joint?

7 **YOUR STARTER FOR**

What was the name of the village in the Vienna Woods, site of a hunting lodge where the bodies of Crown Prince Rupert and a seventeen-year-old girl, Maria Von Vetsera, were found in 1889?

Classical drama

a Which word, nowadays applied to the chief person in a play, meant, literally, the 'first actor' in ancient Greek drama, as opposed to the less important performers?

b What Latin phrase describes the God who descended in a type of crane at the end of a classical play to rescue mortals and resolve complicated plots?

c What name was given to the 'dancing place' of the Greek theatres, which was originally circular with an altar to Dionysus at its centre?

8 **YOUR STARTER FOR**

Who, in his *Discours de la Méthode* of 1637 proposed to reconstruct the whole of philosophy on the basis of a few self-evident intuitions, such as the existence of the self in consciousness – 'cogito ergo sum', or, 'I think therefore I am'?

Famous ships

a Anchored off Gibraltar, HMS *Tiger* and HMS *Fearless* became, in 1966 and 1968, the venues for discussions between Harold Wilson and which African politician?

b Deliberately allowed to freeze into ice in order that it might drift northwards with the current, which ship was specially designed for Fridtjof Nansen's (Freet-yoff Nanssen's) attempt to reach the North Pole between 1893 and 1896?

c *Rainbow Warrior,* the Greenpeace campaign ship, was sunk by French agents in July 1985 while at harbour in which port?

9 **YOUR STARTER FOR**

In 1955, General George Grivas founded the underground organization EOKA to fight for the independence from Britain of which Mediterranean island?

Astronomy

a What do astronomers measure in order to ascertain the length of a sidereal (si-deer-real) year?

b In which constellation was a supernova recorded by Chinese and Korean astronomers in 1054, the remnants of this explosion being still visible today as the crab nebula?

c In 1572, which astronomer saw a 'new star', brighter than Venus, where no star was supposed to be, in the constellation Cassiopeia, thus showing to be wrong an ancient idea that no change in the heavens could occur?

10 YOUR STARTER FOR

In children's literature, Julian, Dick, Anne, George and Timmy are collectively known as what?

Ores

a Worked extensively at Almaden in Spain, cinnabar is a red, crystalline form of the ore of which metal?

b A residual rock formed by weathering in various regions, what is the main ore of aluminium and its compounds?

c Occurring as blue-grey, cubic crystals, and frequently containing silver and accessory metals, what is the main ore and chief source of lead?

11 YOUR STARTER FOR

What word, in general use today, originates from a member of a Hindu sect who strangled travellers as sacrifices to Kali, the Goddess of Destruction?

Royal weddings

a Which English king married Berengaria of Navarre in Cyprus?

b Which English king married his cousin, Dorothea of Celle (Seller), divorcing and imprisoning her 12 years later?

c Which English king married Alexandra, eldest daughter of Christian IX of Denmark?

12 YOUR STARTER FOR

What name is given to an equation involving the square, or second power, of the unknown quantity?

Horses

a In Norse mythology, what was the name of the eight-legged horse belonging to Odin?

b How did William III's horse, Sorrel, indirectly cause the King's death in 1702?

c According to a poem by Robert Browning, what did a horse called Roland help to do?

13 **YOUR STARTER FOR 10**
Which historic act was performed by Chief Justice Michael Corbett on 10 May 1994?

BONUS QUESTIONS
British politics
a Which British prime minister resigned his army commission in 1899 to enter politics and became MP for Oldham in the General Election of the following year?
b Who was the last Labour politician before 1979 to hold the post of Chancellor of the Exchequer?
c In Government circles, what is the more usual title for a treasurer of Her Majesty's Household?

14 **YOUR STARTER FOR 10**
Which soccer club owner and media mogul turned politician led the coalition headed by his party Forza Italia to victory in the 1994 Italian General Election?

BONUS QUESTIONS
Literature
a What unusual happening occurs in the opening sentence of George Orwell's *1984*?
b The final chapter of which novel, published in 1847, begins with the words, 'Reader, I married him'?
c Give the second line of the poem by W. H. Davies entitled 'Leisure', which begins 'What is this life if, full of care, …'.

15 **YOUR STARTER FOR 10**
In which London cemetery did the tomb of Karl Marx become a place of pilgrimage for visiting Communist leaders until the 1990s?

BONUS QUESTIONS
Mind games
a Word association tests were pioneered by which psychologist, born at Kesswil in Switzerland in 1875?
b The Swiss psychiatrist Hermann Rorschach devised, and lends his name to, a diagnostic procedure for psychological disorders – a method involving the analysis of patients' responses to which stimuli?
c Zener (zee-ner) cards – featuring squares, crosses, circles and other symbols – are used experimentally in which field?

16 YOUR STARTER FOR

Which native Australian bird nests on the ground, is brilliantly coloured and has acquired its name from the distinctively shaped tail belonging to the male?

Drownings

a Which fictional military character leaves his wife when he hears of the death of her servant, disappears and is presumed to have drowned, but is killed by his 'widow's' suitor when he reappears?

b Who was presumed drowned when his clothing was found on a Miami beach in 1974, only to be found in Australia using a false passport?

c Which rock star drowned in his own swimming pool in Hartfield, Essex in July 1969?

17 YOUR STARTER FOR

Which cartoon hero was created by René Goscinny (Renay Gosseenee) and illustrator Albert Uderzo (Albair Udairzo)?

Famous figures with nicknames

a Which pre-Socratic Greek thinker – characteristically pessimistic in his vision of the human condition – is known as 'The Dark One' or, more usually, 'The Weeping Philosospher'?

b Born in Washington DC in 1854, which American composer and bandmaster became known as 'The March King'?

c In office from 1829 to 1837, which US president was nicknamed 'Old Hickory'?

18 YOUR STARTER FOR

What do Esplanade, Castle Hill, Lawn Market, Parliament Square, High Street and Canongate add up to in Edinburgh, and run from the castle to Holyrood House?

Germany

a Name the German scholar who, in 1932, submitted a geographical dissertation on the structure of settlements in southern Germany. Since then his ideas have been verified, extended and used to analyse the pattern of 'Central Places' within cities.

b Which German region in Baden-Wurttemberg is bound to the west and south by the River Rhine and by the Neckar Valley to the north?

c Which German seaport on the south side of the Elbe estuary acts as an outport for Hamburg?

19

YOUR STARTER FOR

Although used by the ancient Egyptians and Greeks, which method of surveying, developed as a science by Dutch mathematician Willebrord Snell, uses lengths and angles between points usually situated on hilltops?

Monasteries and monks

a Green and yellow types of which herb liqueur are produced by monks at Voiron, near Grenoble?

b Which Dominican Friar led a 1494 Florentine revolt that expelled the ruling Medici family?

c What is the popular name for the branch of Cistercian monks, founded in 1140 at the monastery of Soligny La Trappe and reorganized in the seventeenth century by Armand de France, who practised extreme austerity of diet, penitential exercise and absolute silence?

20

YOUR STARTER FOR

Which thriller writer came across many of his future plots while a Reuter's correspondent in the 1960s, his time in Nigeria during the civil war giving him the idea for *The Dogs of War*?

Geographical name changes

a Called Lourenço Marques until 1975, what is the current name of the capital of Mozambique?

b Sverdlovsk, a town in the Eastern foothills of the Urals where Tsar Nicholas II and his family were murdered in 1918, was known at that time by which name, readopted in 1991?

c A former French colony in West Africa, which country was renamed Burkina Faso in 1984?

SPARE STARTER QUESTIONS

21 Going in a clockwise direction around mainland Britain, what completes this list of coastal extremities: Ardnamurchan Point, Dunnet Head, Lowestoft Ness...?

22 Which nursery rhyme has been ascribed to a sixteenth-century physician and entomologist, also known as Thomas Mouffet or Moffitt?

23 Where in South London were a South American river, a Scottish fishing port, and a Balkan Republic assembled by Mrs Beresford?

24 Which contemporary film director bought Rosebud, the sledge used in *Citizen Kane,* to remind him that 'Quality in movies comes first'?
25 If number 38 is a Scottish village and number 72 is Copenhagen, what is 92?

Game eleven

1

YOUR STARTER FOR 10

What was officially opened on 6 May 1994 when the Queen and President Mitterand cut a ribbon of Calais lace?'

Policemen and detectives

a What is the surname of the police officer whom Jean Valjean struggles to elude in Victor Hugo's novel *Les Misérables*?

b Which private eye is one of the central characters in the 1941 film with which John Huston made his début as a director?

c Which television private detective of the 1980s provided a phone-in problem-solving service on Radio West?

2

YOUR STARTER FOR 10

Which word, originally used to describe a piratical sixteenth-century privateer, has come to be used for the practice of a minority in a legislature using extended debate to block or delay action on a proposed bill?

Missing fifths

a Which child completes this quintet? Alexis, Olga, Tatiana, Maria.

b Which MP completed this quintet? Pym, Hampden, Haselrig, Holles.

c And finally, for 5 points, who completes this quintet? Chico, Harpo, Groucho, Gummo.

3

YOUR STARTER FOR 10

Which English scientist was given the sobriquet Darwin's Bulldog for his championing of evolution following the publication of *The Origin of Species*? In 1869 he coined the word agnostic.

Parliament

a On what days (give both days for the 5 points) does Prime Minister's Question Time take place when the House of Commons is in session?

b Harking back to a more warlike age, the opposing front benches in the House are the length of two what apart?

c What, precisely, must an MP do before he or she speaks if he or she wishes to challenge the ruling of the Chair during a division?

4

YOUR STARTER FOR

Which school, whose former pupils include the actor Jason Connery and the author William Boyd, was founded in 1934 by the educationalist Kurt Hahn?

Philadelphia

a Who, after John Hinkley shot him, reputedly quoted W. C. Fields' remark about death, 'All in all, I'd rather be in Philadelphia'?

b Who won an Oscar in 1994 for the Best Original Song for 'Streets of Philadelphia'?

c Which film musical, starring Bing Crosby and Grace Kelly, was a remake of the Katharine Hepburn film *The Philadelphia Story*?

5

YOUR STARTER FOR

Which London concert hall was built by the Bechstein piano company and bore their name until anti-German feeling resulted in a change of name in 1917?

Countries

a Which is the largest country through which the Tropic of Cancer passes?

b Which is the largest country through which the Greenwich Meridian passes?

c Which is the largest country through which the Tropic of Capricorn passes?

6

YOUR STARTER FOR

Christy Mahon, who arrives in a village in Mayo boasting of having killed his father, is the leading character in which play by J. M. Synge?

Forgeries

a What was denounced as a fake in the bulletin of the British Museum in 1953?

b Which forgery was published on 24 October 1924, five days before the General Election?

c Who was the brilliant Dutch forger who specialized in 'lost Vermeers', even selling some of his works to Goering?

7

YOUR STARTER FOR

In a sporting context, what was won by a Russian ballet dancer in 1970, an ancient city in Asia Minor in 1979, and the object sought by Jason and the Argonauts in 1982?

Literary ladies

a How was Dolores Haxe better known in an eponymous novel, first published in Paris in 1955?

b Which novel, first published in 1740, with the subtitle 'Virtue Rewarded' takes its title from the first name of one of the characters, Miss Andrews?

c What is the name of the first Mrs De Winter, commemorated in the title of a 1938 novel in which she does not appear?

8

YOUR STARTER FOR

George II was the last reigning monarch to occupy which palace just up the Thames from Richmond?

Charity events

a Who, launching an appeal to help the starving in Africa in 1991, said, 'It would be a lot easier if we could auction Gazza'?

b Whose is the first voice to be heard on the 1984 Band Aid single?

c Name the stadium in Philadelphia that staged the American Live Aid concert in 1985?

9

YOUR STARTER FOR

Which pass, the carriage road over which was built between 1800 and 1807 on Napoleon's orders, reaches a height of over 2000 metres and links Brig in Switzerland with Iselle in Italy?

Famous resignations

a Which famous speech began with the words 'at long last, I am able to say a few words on my own'?

b Which American vice-president resigned in the face of tax evasion charges in 1973?

c Who resigned as head of state after a referendum defeat in 1969?

10 YOUR STARTER FOR

What do Neil, of the TV series *The Young Ones,* singer K. D. Lang and American poet and painter E. E. Cummings have in common in the way they write their names?

Minerals and gems

a Which mineral, with the chemical name aluminium fluosilicate, is usually yellow, but pink if it has been heated, and is used as a gem stone when transparent?

b What name is given to all non-red corundum gem stones?

c Which variety of lignite used in ornamentation occurs in large quantities near Whitby?

11 YOUR STARTER FOR

The Colossus of Rhodes, one of the Seven Wonders of the World, is a statue of which God?

Instruments

a Which instrument, that can be used for reducing or enlarging drawings or plans, consists of rigid bars adjustably connected by pin joints?

b Which instrument linked with the sixteenth-century English mathematician Leonard Digges consists of a telescope mounted so as to swivel both horizontally and vertically?

c By the second half of the eighteenth century, the sextant, with an arc spanning 60 degrees, had replaced which instrument with a 45-degree arc?

12 YOUR STARTER FOR

Xestobium rufovillosum, found chiefly in the wooden beams of old buildings or furniture where it makes a ticking sound as it burrows, is better known as what?

Lakes

a What term is applied to a lake found on the flood plain of a river and formed by a cut-off meander?

b Which two lakes are linked by the Welland Ship Canal, part of the St Lawrence Seaway?

c In the Lake District, which body of water lies above Great Langdale in the shadow of Pavey Ark?

13

YOUR STARTER FOR
Who was appointed one of Britain's commissioners in July 1994, succeeding Bruce Millan, and thus able to join his wife in Europe?

BONUS QUESTIONS

Three famous Swiss
a Which Swiss mathematician first derived the theorem, named after him, which implies that, in a horizontally flowing fluid, a decrease in fluid pressure is accompanied by an increase in fluid velocity?
b Which Swiss artist wrote 'Drawing is an active line, on a walk, moving freely without a goal'?
c Which composer, born of Swiss parents, wrote 'Pacific 231', an impression of a steam locomotive in action and 'Rugby' which reflected his love of speed and manly sports?

14

YOUR STARTER FOR
In sculpture, intaglio is where the design is incized into the block. What name is given to its opposite form of relief sculpture usually applied to gem stones such as agate and onyx?

BONUS QUESTIONS

Economics and finance
a In economics, what phrase is usually used to express Gresham's Law in simple terms?
b For what reason did the US Government issue paper money – given the colloquial name of greenbacks – in the 1860s?
c Who was British prime minister when sterling was taken off the Gold Standard in September 1931?

15

YOUR STARTER FOR
In the middle high German poem, the 'Nibelungenlied', which prince is murdered by Hagen partly at the behest of Brunhild?

BONUS QUESTIONS

The military
a In what respect was warrant officer Keith Payne of the Australian army unique among Vietnam war combatants?
b Which poet, who was awarded the Military Cross in October 1918, was killed on the Sambre Canal near Ors a week before Armistice Day?
c What inscription appears on the George Cross?

16 YOUR STARTER FOR
Invented about 1710 by George Graham, which mechanical device, the forerunner of the modern planetarium, demonstrates the motions of the heavenly bodies?

Russian writers

a Which writer, several of whose 'little tragedies' provided the basis for Russian operas, was mortally wounded defending his wife's honour in a duel forced on him by his enemies in 1837?

b *Dead Souls* and *The Government Inspector* are two of the major works of which Ukranian-born writer and dramatist, who lived from 1809 until 1852?

c What was the pen name of the Russian writer Aleksey Maksimovich Peshkov, who, in 1934, became the first President of the Union of Soviet writers?

17 YOUR STARTER FOR
Which modern capital city stands on the site of the ancient city of Tenochtitlan?

Flying firsts

a What aviation first was achieved by Charles Kingsford Smith and Charles Ulm with a crew of two in June 1928?

b June 1939 saw the inauguration of which company's transatlantic flying-boat service?

c Which aircraft made its first flight into Heathrow on 23 January 1970?

18 YOUR STARTER FOR
The long-awaited autobiography of which film actor, published in September 1994 and detailing his many love affairs, is called *Songs My Mother Taught Me*?

Fictional schools

a Which private boarding school in Dickens' *Nicholas Nickleby* is callously controlled by Mr Wackford Squeers?

b Charles Chipping, a long-serving teacher dedicated to the welfare of his pupils at Brookfield School, is the central character in which novella by James Hilton?

c Danny, Toots, Plug, Wilfrid and Cuthbert Cringeworthy are perennial pupils at which educational establishment, founded on 14 February 1954?

19 YOUR STARTER FOR

In May 1974, which independent republican beat his socialist rival François Mitterand in the French presidential elections?

Flags

a The flag of which South American country bears the motto 'Ordem e Progresso'?

b Specifically, which bird appears on the state flag of Western Australia?

c What appears inside the white star in the centre of the flag of Northern Ireland?

20 YOUR STARTER FOR

Which religion's fundamental doctrine consists of the four Noble Truths?

US presidential elections

a Which presidential candidate polled almost ten million votes standing as an 'American independent' in 1968?

b On which party ticket did Norman Thomas contest every presidential election between 1928 and 1948?

c What was the name of the Texan billionaire who stood as an independent candidate in the 1992 US Presidential Election, polling 19 per cent of the vote, the best showing for a third candidate since 1912?

SPARE STARTER QUESTIONS

21 Stamford in Lincolnshire represented which fictional town in a classic BBC TV serial, first shown in 1994?

22 Which trignometrical ratio is the inverse of sine?

23 Which rock superstar, with Reeves Gabreus and Tony and Hunt Soles, formed the band Tin Machine in 1989?

24 Some street name plaques in the city of Chester are in two languages. Which two languages?

25 How is hydrated magnesium silicate known when used in the bathroom?

Game twelve

1

YOUR STARTER FOR

Which American Colonel said 'I came here to tell you the truth – the good, the bad and the ugly' when giving evidence to the so-called Irangate hearings in the summer of 1987?

BONUS QUESTIONS

Royal towns

a The suffix 'Regis' meaning 'of the King' can be found in 12 English place names, of which 4 are in one county. Which county?

b To which spa town in Kent did Edward VII bestow the prefix 'Royal' in 1909?

c Which monarch bestowed the 'Royal' prefix on Leamington Spa when the spa resort was at the height of its popularity?

2

YOUR STARTER FOR

Cardinal Reginald Pole was the last Catholic holder of which ecclesiastical post?

BONUS QUESTIONS

Brothers

a Which highly successful company, bearing the name of its founders, was established by the brothers Charles and Maurice in 1970?

b How were two brothers from Northumberland part of sporting history in the London Borough of Brent on 30 July 1966?

c Who wrote the best-selling book *The Brotherhood,* an investigation into British freemasonry?

3

YOUR STARTER FOR

Which capital city was originally named Britannia but was renamed in honour of a British prime minister who held office from 1828 to 1830 who is best remembered for defeating Napoleon in the Battle of Waterloo?

BONUS QUESTIONS

Architecture

a With which capital city would you most closely identify the work of the architect Oscar Niemeyer?

b Which twentieth-century American architect and engineer developed the geodesic dome?

c Which 'new' capital city was designed and built by Edward Lutyens and Herbert Baker?

4

YOUR STARTER FOR 10
Which writer was the President of the South African Liberal Party when it was declared illegal in 1968?

BONUS QUESTIONS

Judicial inquiries and reports
a What is the subject of the judicial inquiry set up under Lord Justice Scott in 1992, which began hearings in the summer of 1993?
b Which former judge was the author of a report into the Brixton riots of 1981?
c Lord Denning who was Master of the Rolls from 1962–82 conducted an inquiry into which political scandal of 1963?

5

YOUR STARTER FOR 10
Which region of the electromagnetic spectrum lies in the wavelength range of approximately 5 to 400 nanometres, that is, between X-rays and visible light waves?

BONUS QUESTIONS

Classical music premières
a Vaughan Williams's *Fantasy on a Theme of Thomas Tallis* and Holst's *Choral Fantasia* both had their premières at which musical festival?
b Which opera was first performed in Milan in 1926, two years after the death of the composer?
c The first performance of which ballet, in Paris on 29 May 1913, was the occasion of what has been described as 'one of the greatest riots in the history of the theatre'?

6

YOUR STARTER FOR 10
What is the name of the dance performed by the All Blacks rugby union team before every match?

BONUS QUESTIONS

Svens
a In which soap did bronzed Sven the sheep-shearer, played by Daniel O'Grady, turn up to help the Sugdens?
b In which spoof radio quiz show does the lovely Sven sometimes take over the scoring from the equally lovely Samantha?
c Gloria Josephine May Svensson was the original name of which

Hollywood movie star, most famous for her role as the fading movie queen Norma Desmond in the 1950 film *Sunset Boulevard*?

7 **YOUR STARTER FOR**
Which Russian reigned jointly with his half-brother Ivan V until becoming sole ruler upon Ivan's death in 1696, was proclaimed Emperor in 1721 and was succeeded four years later by his wife, who became Catherine I?

Questions
a According to tradition, who asked the question 'Domine, quo vadis'?
b Which artist asked three questions in the title of his work begun in 1898, which he regarded as his finest canvas?
c What title is given to the question that was solved by Oedipus, thus saving the Thebans?

8 **YOUR STARTER FOR**
Although trained as an engineer, which Vienna-born philosopher came to the subject through the study of philosophy of mathematics with Bertrand Russell, and was Professor of Philosophy at Cambridge from 1939–47?

Asian political leaders
a The father of which Asian Prime Minister was himself the Prime Minister of their country before being overthrown by the military in 1977 and executed in 1979?
b In which country did Khaleda Zia succeed her assassinated husband as leader of his political party, becoming Prime Minister in March 1991?
c Who succeeded Ferdinand Marcos as President of the Philippines in 1986, and was confirmed in the post until 30 June 1992, the first woman to hold the office?

9 **YOUR STARTER FOR**
Now used to mean unimportant details or trifles, which word ultimately derives from a modern plural of the Latin for 'the place where three roads meet'?

Rocket sites
a Which village in the Rostock district was the site of the chief German research and testing facility for rockets and missiles – the so-called V-Weapons – which were eventually used against Britain?

b By what name was Cape Canaveral, the site of operations for the US space programme, known between 1963 and 1973?

c What is the name of the space centre in Kazakhstan that many historic Soviet space flights were launched from, including the first artificial satellite in 1957 (Sputnik), the first manned orbital flight in 1961 (Yuri Gagarin) and the first woman in space in 1963 (Valentina Tereshkova)?

10   YOUR STARTER FOR 10

After becoming a British subject in 1726, which German-born musician was appointed a composer of the Chapel Royal and wrote the *Coronation Anthems for George II*, which include 'Zadok the Priest'?

BONUS QUESTIONS

Mountains with a planetary link

a Olympus Mons, with a diameter of over 600 kilometres and a height of over 20 000 metres, is the largest known volcano in the solar system and it is on which planet?

b Reaching a height of over 11 000 metres and taking its name from the Scottish physicist who formulated electromagnetic theory, what is the highest mountain on Venus?

c The 'mountains of the moon', or the Ruwenzori Range, rising to over 16 000 feet, border Zaïre and which other country?

11   YOUR STARTER FOR 10

Tibor Fischer's black comedy, *Under the Frog*, a contender for the 1993 Booker Prize, chronicles the Russian suppression of which revolution in 1956?

BONUS QUESTIONS

Massacres

a The Saint Bartholemew's Day Massacre of French Huguenots in Paris, in August 1572, is claimed to have been plotted by which regent of France?

b Manchester's Peterloo Massacre of 1819 saw the cavalry's brutal dispersal of a political rally that was being presided over by which radical leader?

c What disguises were used by some of Al Capone's men during the 1929 Saint Valentine's Day Massacre?

12

YOUR STARTER FOR

What name is given to the typical form of a jellyfish because of its resemblance to the snake-like curls of a gorgon's head?

Christmas songs

a According to the song, what did my true love send to me on the seventh day of Christmas?

b In 'The Holly and the Ivy', which line follows 'The rising of the sun'?

c Which traditional Christmas song includes the line 'Field and fountain, moor and mountain'?

13

YOUR STARTER FOR

In somatotyping – a system used for classifying human body shapes and physiques – what is the third component along with mesomorphy and ectomorphy?

The Islamic religion

a The five pillars of Islam are the duties incumbent on every Muslim; the fourth of these, the 'Saum', involves fasting during which month of the Islamic calendar?

b Devout Muslims are expected to pray five times a day – at dawn, midday, afternoon, sunset and evening – and the ritual prayer is the second of the five pillars. How is it known in Arabic?

c The Khawarij (ka-waar-rij) sect added a sixth pillar, not accepted by the general community, called 'Jihad'. How is this usually translated into English?

14

YOUR STARTER FOR

Which famous seventeenth-century sitter requested the portrait painter Sir Peter Lely to 'remark all these roughnesses, pimples, warts, and everything as you see me'?

City planning

a Which residential district of London, lying mostly within the city of Westminster, contains many squares and crescents and was designed in the 1820s by Thomas Cubitt?

b Which architect planned the Indian city of Chandigarh in the 1950s, dividing it into 36 rectangular sectors?

c In the late eighteenth century, the French military engineer Pierre-Charles l'Enfant created a design incorporating wide avenues and a rectangular grid of streets for which American city?

15 YOUR STARTER FOR

Which British film was nominated for an Oscar for Best Foreign Film in 1994?

The Russian, or Cyrillic, alphabet

a The Cyrillic character that looks like the Latin 'B' is the equivalent of which Latin letter?

b The Latin letter 'S' has an equivalent in the Cyrillic alphabet that is written as which Latin character?

c How is the Cyrillic character that is pronounced 'N' (en) written in Cyrillic?

16 YOUR STARTER FOR

A Caribbean island and its capital city have, over the years, exchanged names. The original name of the island was San Juan, what was the original name of its capital?

Roman writers

a Which poet was banished to Tomi on the Black Sea by the Emperor Augustus on undisclosed charges of immorality, one of his best-known works being *Ars Amatoria* (Art of Love)?

b Which Roman poet is particularly famous for his lyric poetry, speaking of his love for Lesbia in 25 of his poems?

c Which Roman poet turned down the post of Private Secretary to Augustus and has as his most frequent themes of his 'odes' and verse 'epistles' love, friendship, philosophy and the art of poetry?

17 YOUR STARTER FOR

The widely banned pesticide dichlorodiphenyltrichloroethane is better known by what abbreviation?

Islands

a How was Ireland described in the title of a 1904 Shaw play, a phrase he borrowed from an earlier work of Leon Paul Blouet?

b Which island was the centre of the Minoan civilization?

c The Republic of Haiti and the Dominican Republic share which Caribbean island?

18

YOUR STARTER FOR 10

Although not necessarily an MP, the Lord Advocate is the Scottish equivalent of which law officer in England and Wales?

Chinese arts and crafts

a The art of sericulture, which, according to Chinese legend, was introduced by the wife of the 'Yellow Emperor', refers to the care and breeding of what?

b Which landscape design, a legend of lovers transformed into swallows, was developed by Thomas Minton while serving his apprenticeship at Thomas Turner's Caughley pottery, Shropshire, around 1779, in imitation of the designs on Chinese pottery?

c Which stone has been used since Neolithic times in China for carving ornaments etc., the object being regarded as intrinsically valuable because the hardness, durability and beauty of the stone is said to reflect human values?

19

YOUR STARTER FOR 10

In which of Shakespeare's plays does Florizel, the Prince of Bohemia, fall in love with Perdita?

Paintings

a Which painting, one of a pair produced by Goya around 1800, has the face awkwardly superimposed on the body, suggesting that the identity of the sensuous lady had been disguised?

b Which famous painting by Botticelli shows a naked lady standing on a large shell in the sea framed by various mythical figures?

c Which painting by Manet shows a naked lady picnicking under trees with two gentlemen friends?

20

YOUR STARTER FOR 10

Often worn by golfers (for whom it is almost compulsory to wear silly clothes), what is the difference between plus-twos and plus-fours?

Pubs and taverns

a Which pub name has its origins in the coat of arms on the Earls of Warwick?

b Who was the hostess of the Boar's Head Tavern in Eastcheap, at one time betrothed to Falstaff and later the wife of Pistol?

c Who, according to one of his biographers, Sir John Hawkins, espoused the view that '...a tavern chair is the throne of human felicity'?

SPARE STARTER QUESTIONS

21 Which statesman, essayist and philosopher, born in 1561, held the titles Baron Verulam and Viscount St Albans?

22 Mexico borders three countries. The USA is one, name either of the other two.

23 Who succeeded Norman Willis as General Secretary of the Trades Union Congress in 1993?

24 What is the more common name for the medical condition hemicrania (hemi-crane-ia)?

25 What term is applied to the decorated central division of an entablature, between the architrave and the cornice?

Game thirteen

1

Who vowed, after being sworn in as its President, that his country would never again be the 'skunk of the world'?

Shared surnames

a Which surname is shared by three men – one a thirteenth-century philosopher and experimental scientist, another an essayist and seventeenth-century statesman, and the third a painter who died in 1992?

b What surname is shared by an early nineteenth-century British admiral, a British novelist and poet, and an American film comic who was one half of a famous duo?

c A nineteenth-century prison reformer, a twentieth-century writer of verse plays and a contemporary writer, actor and comedian all share which surname?

2

YOUR STARTER FOR

Which compilation of over 200 poems from the thirteenth century provided the basis for a cantata first performed in 1937 and composed by Carl Orff?

Basic foodstuffs

a What is the name of the traditional North African dish normally made with semolina and cooked in a special earthenware pot?

b What name is given to the cornmeal porridge that is the traditional basic dish of Northern Italy?

c What name is given to the kernels of corn from which the hull and germ have been removed by a caustic agent that is a staple in the southern United States where, as grits, it can be boiled and served with butter or shaped into cakes and fried?

3

YOUR STARTER FOR

What term describes the arrangement whereby an MP who wishes to be absent from voting agrees with an opposition MP for them to do the same, in so doing neutralizing the votes?

Names of symphonies and concerts

a Bruckner's Symphony No. 3 in D minor is sometimes referred to by the name of the composer to whom it was dedicated. Who was he?

b Whose 'Ebony' clarinet concerto was written for Woody Herman?

c Whose first symphony is known as the 'Sea' Symphony?

4

YOUR STARTER FOR

Usually found in tropical rainforests, what name is given to plants that grow on other plants merely for support but obtain water and other nutrients from rain and also from debris that collects on supporting plants?

Popes

a In 1059, Pope Nicholas II promulgated a Papal Bull that restricted Papal electors to whom?

b What name is given to the assembly of Cardinals that elects the Pope, created by Gregory X at the fourteenth Ecumenical Council at Lyons in 1274?

c Prior to John Paul II, the last non-Italian Pope was Adrian VI in 1522. What was his nationality?

5

YOUR STARTER FOR

A man living with his second wife and confronted by the ghost of his first, raised by the eccentric medium Madame Arcati, is the situation explored in which stage comedy of 1941, written by Noël Coward?

Famous Wilsons

a C. T. R. Wilson is said to have been inspired to invent which radiation detector after working at the observatory on the misty summit of Ben Nevis?

b Which American President had the middle name Wilson?

c Which novelist, whose first and last names were John Wilson, but who was known by his middle two names, wrote *The Kingdom of the Wicked,* an account of the Christian struggle against Imperial Rome, among other works?

6

YOUR STARTER FOR

Originally a nomadic people who established power through a series of successful invasions, what was the name of China's ruling dynasty from 1644 until they were overthrown in 1912?

Nineteenth-century South African history

a What name was given to the emigration from Cape Colony of some 10 000 Boers between 1835 and the early 1840s to fresh pasture-lands, regarded by Afrikaaners as the origin of their nationhood?

b Known affectionately as 'Oom (Uncle) Paul', and a builder of the Afrikaaner nation, who went to Holland in 1900 as he was too old to keep up with the guerrilla struggle in the Boer War, dying in Switzerland in 1904?

c What was the name of the friend and collaborator of Cecil Rhodes who impetuously led 500 mounted men to invade the Transvaal in 1895, when he and his men were defeated and captured?

7 YOUR STARTER FOR

Belgian Foreign Minister Willy Claes was appointed in September 1994 to succeed General Manfred Worner as Secretary-General of which organization?

Precious metals and hallmarks

a What word pertains to the testing of precious metals to be sure of their quality?

b The head of which animal came to be recognized as the mark of the London Assay Office after being introduced in the year 1300?

c What name was given to a piece of smooth rock of fine grain which was, however, strongly abrasive, so that when a piece of silver or gold to be tested was rubbed on it, some of the metal was transferred to it in a bright streak?

8 YOUR STARTER FOR

Which sport was born out of the 'broken time' dispute of the 1890s and has since spread to France, Australia and New Zealand, among others, but in England has remained principally in the North?

Famous links

a How were Strettin and Trieste linked in a speech at Westminster College, Fulton, Missouri in March 1946?

b What is the link between Oxford at 92 and London at 104?

c What linked St Joseph, Missouri, to Sacramento, California, for 18 months from April 1860 until October 1861?

9 **YOUR STARTER FOR 10**

What word, when used in sculpture, means an inner structure used for models made of soft material that are of sufficient size to require support, but when referring to electromechanical devices means the coils, usually rotating, of a dynamo or electric motor?

Castles and palaces

a In which former royal palace, built chiefly between the thirteenth and mid fourteenth centuries, will you find the Court of Lions, the Court of the Myrtles and the Hall of Secrets?

b Which castle's walls enclose two areas known as the Upper Ward and the Lower Ward?

c Which royal residence was designed by Prince Albert and the builder Thomas Cubitt, but was used by only one monarch?

10 **YOUR STARTER FOR 10**

Why is psephology – the statistical study of voting and elections – so called?

Organizations

a Which international religious organization, founded in the USA in 1899, is named after the Old Testament commander who defeated the Midianites?

b Which penal reform organization, founded in 1866, is named after an eighteenth-century high sheriff of Bedfordshire?

c Which former priest was the Chairman of the Campaign for Nuclear Disarmament from 1987 to 1990?

11 **YOUR STARTER FOR 10**

What connects Kipling in 1907, W. B. Yeats in 1923, T. S. Eliot in 1948, Hemingway in 1954 and William Golding in 1983?

The stately homes of England

a In which county did P. G. Wodehouse site Blanding Castle, country seat of Lord Emsworth?

b In which county is the eighteenth-century Palladian mansion Holkham Hall?

c What is the name of the twentieth-century 'castle' in Devon built by Sir Edward Lutyens and overlooking the Teign Gorge?

12 YOUR STARTER FOR
Which single word describes all of the following? A resin exuded from pine trees, a speech intended to influence or persuade, the forward plunge of a ship in a longitudinal direction, and the position of a single sound in the complete range of sound.

Famous people associated with the present-day county of Cumbria

a Which writer, born in 1866 in London, married solicitor William Heelis and lived at Hill Top, near Sawrey, on the west side of Windermere?

b Who moved to Kendal from his native Blackburn in 1941 and is famous for his illustrated guides to the Lakeland fells?

c Which town, now in Cumbria, was the birthplace of Stan Laurel in 1890 and now has a Laurel and Hardy museum?

13 YOUR STARTER FOR
What made their television début in December 1963, were created by Terry Nation, and were once described as being 'like a bubble-car on castors'?

Horseracing

a Name either of the two classic English horseraces that are for fillies only?

b Which 1983 film tells the true story of an Australian racehorse, winner of the Melbourne Cup in 1930?

c The naming of racehorses is controlled by Weatherbys and they restrict the length of names to how many characters, including spaces?

14 YOUR STARTER FOR
The sum of the binary numbers 100 and 10 is equal to what in decimal numbers?

British battles

a Which battle was fought two miles east of Market Drayton in 1459, resulting in a heavy defeat of the Lancastrian forces led by Lord Audley?

b The largest and bloodiest battle ever fought on British soil took place in a snowstorm on Palm Sunday 1461. Where did the engagement take place?

c The last British King to die in combat lost his life in which battle?

15

YOUR STARTER FOR 10

Which civilization flourished in what is now Yucatan (Southern Mexico), Belize and Guatemala several hundred years before a rapid decline about the year 900?

Phrases and expressions

BONUS QUESTIONS

a Which American expression meaning exactly on time is said to have originated in the broadcasting studio when the producer put his finger to a part of his face to indicate a programme was running to schedule?

b The phrase 'expletive deleted', widely used in the 1970s, entered popular use after the publication of transcripts relating to what?

c What expression is used for a period of extreme heat and humidity in the temperate latitudes in August, usually about the middle of the month?

16

YOUR STARTER FOR 10

Which term, from the Greek for 'running back again', describes a word, phrase or verse that reads the same both forwards and backwards?

Cities

BONUS QUESTIONS

a Which ancient city, once the centre of an Arab kingdom, is often referred to as the 'Rose-Red' city?

b Which French city was the capital of the province of Aquitania under the Romans and was known by them as Burdigala?

c Which North American city was known as Bytown from 1827 until the mid 1850s when it was rechristened, taking its name from an Algonquian-speaking Indian tribe?

17

YOUR STARTER FOR 10

Who was elected the President of the USA 16 years after he was first elected Vice-President in 1952?

Parliament

BONUS QUESTIONS

a Which government officer holds the title Parliamentary Secretary to the Treasury?

b Which parliamentary official holds the title Chairman of Ways and Means?

c According to parliamentary convention, who would occupy the seat 'below the gangway' in the Commons?

18

YOUR STARTER FOR 10

Who wrote the lines 'Far, far beneath in the abysmal sea,/ his ancient, dreamless, uninvaded sleep/ the Kraken sleepeth' from which John Wyndham took the title of his novel *The Kraken Wakes*?

Types of songs

a Which Italian word is used for a drinking song, for example Alfredo and Violetta's 'Libiamo' in Verdi's *La Traviata*?

b Which French word is used for a boating song, especially of Venetian gondoliers, its rhythm imitating the motion of a boat?

c Which German word is used for a cradle song, the French word *berceuse* being its equivalent, well-known examples being written by Hugo Wolf and Brahms?

19

YOUR STARTER FOR 10

Which opera company, named after its impresario founder, established a home in London's Savoy theatre when it opened in 1881 with a production of Gilbert and Sullivan's *Patience*?

Children's literature

a Which children's book, published in 1906, centres on Roberta, Peter and Phyllis who are forced to move with their mother to a simple country cottage near a tunnel?

b Who was the wise, genial old man, created by Joel Chandler Harris, who told stories about Brer Rabbit and Brer Fox?

c What was the title of the 1972 sequel to Roald Dahl's children's novel *Charlie and the Chocolate Factory*?

20

YOUR STARTER FOR 10

The abbreviation S.A. can be seen after the names of companies in French-speaking countries. What does S.A. stand for?

Deaths

a How, according to fable, did the Greek dramatist Aeschylus meet his death?

b Frederick Louis, Prince of Wales and son of George II died as the result of a sporting accident. What happened to him?

c Who, in September 1927, was strangled by her own scarf when it became entangled in the spoked wheels of her sports car?

SPARE STARTER QUESTIONS

21 In signal processing, noise that is spread evenly across a given frequency range is known as 'white noise'. What name is given to noise biased towards the low-frequency end?

22 Which British publishing house was founded in 1973 and was established for the promotion and publication of the works of women writers?

23 What three things were fundamental to the religious ceremony of pronouncing anathema?

24 Which town between Rotterdam and The Hague gave its name to a type of tin-glazed earthenware first made there early in the seventeenth century?

25 Methane acquired which alternative name because it is formed by the decay of vegetable matter under water?

Game fourteen

1

In English law, the person who sues in a civil action is the plaintiff.
Which term is used for such a person in Scottish courts?

Dams

a The 150-mile long Franklin D. Roosevelt lake lies behind which dam on the Columbia River in Washington State?

b In July 1991, the Overseas Development Agency gave a loan of £234 million towards the cost of building which dam in Malaysia?

c Which country's relations with its neighbours were strained when the flow of the Euphrates was interrupted for one month from 13 January 1990 in order to start filling the Atatürk Dam?

2

YOUR STARTER FOR
Which word was coined by Horace Walpole to describe the facilty of making lucky and unexpected discoveries by accident?

Ancient Greece

a According to Plutarch, how did the Athenian statesman and orator Demosthenes of the fourth century BC overcome a speech defect?

b The philosopher Diogenes, often credited with founding the Cynic School, is said to have carried a lamp around in broad daylight to look for what?

c Students of which philosopher who advocated avoidance of political activity and public life, lived in a simple manner at his school, drinking mainly water and eating barley bread? His name now has connotations of an entirely opposite lifestyle.

3

YOUR STARTER FOR
The passenger pigeon in 1914, the great auk in 1844 and the dodo in the late seventeenth century all suffered which fate?

Geography

a Describe the geographical process of attrition.

b In a limestone cave, how is a feature called a pillar or column formed?

c Striding Edge on Helvellyn, a knife-edged ridge separating adjacent corries, is an example of which geographical feature?

YOUR STARTER FOR

4

Francis I, Emperor of Austria from 1804–35, was also known as Francis II when, from 1792–1806, he was the last holder of which title?

Company shares

a What term is used for an issue of shares in which shareholders must be offered the new shares in proportion to their holding in existing shares, normally at a discount on the current share price?

b What word describes the number of shares or amount of stock that a director of a company must hold in order to be appointed or to continue as such?

c What is defined by the Companies Act 1985 as an 'invitation, offering to the public for subscription or purchase any shares or debentures of a company', which must also contain a description of aims, capital structure and any past history of the venture?

YOUR STARTER FOR

5

In May 1994, the largest museum in the world dedicated to one artist was opened in Pittsburgh, the artist's birthplace. Who is the artist?

Political embarrassments of the 1980s

a Geoffrey Prime, who was convicted in November 1982 of spying for the Russians, was an employee of which government establishment?

b What was the name of the civil servant at the Ministry of Defence who was cleared, in 1985, of breaking the Official Secrets Act by passing information about the sinking of the *General Belgrano*?

c Colette Bowe, an information officer at the DTI, was at the centre of which controversy, which began late in 1985 and led to the resignation of two cabinet ministers?

YOUR STARTER FOR

6

'The Cage', which starred Jeffrey Hunter as Captain Christopher Pike, was the original pilot for which TV sci-fi series, now a cult industry?

Bali

a To which group of islands does Bali belong?

b Bali was the king of which animals in Eastern mythology?

c To whom did Bali, the demon, promise as much land as he could measure in three strides, and thereby became master of heaven, earth and air?

7

YOUR STARTER FOR
If R = 1, Y = 2 and G = 3, what is 6?

Composers
a Which musician published nothing in the last 26 years of his life, from 1931 until his death in 1957, although he is said to have written and destroyed an eighth symphony?
b Which musician wrote scarcely anything for nearly the last 40 years of his life, except for a few religious works, after having composed some 35 successful operas, first performed between 1812 and 1829?
c Which composer, who died in 1901 aged 87, wrote his only comic opera in 1893, aged 80?

8

YOUR STARTER FOR 10
Which politician held the following appointments: Minister of Overseas Development from 1964–5, Minister of Transport from 1965–8, Secretary of State for Employment & Productivity from 1968–70 and Secretary of State for Social Services from 1974–6 until she was dropped from the Cabinet by James Callaghan?

Titles
Give the appropriate title for each of the following:
a The Governor of a district under the Nazi regime.
b. A Moslem ruler descended from Mohammed through his daughter Fatima.
c In the Turkish Empire, a superior military officer or governor of a minor province.

9

YOUR STARTER FOR 10
Founded in 1889 by Charles H. Dow of Dow Jones and Company, which newspaper carried mainly business and economic news until the early years of the Great Depression?

Knights
a British-born, he starred in and directed dozens of films. He was knighted for his services to the cinema in 1975, although he had only appeared in two films in the preceding 20 years. Who was he?

b Which English humorous novelist was knighted at the same time as Chaplin, only a month before his death and 20 years after he had taken American citizenship?

c Which former England footballer was knighted in the Queen's Birthday Honours list in 1994?

10 YOUR STARTER FOR 10

Which American playwright, a Nobel Prize winner in 1936, wrote a trilogy based on the *Orestia* trilogy of Aeschylus, set in the New England of the American Civil War, the title of this work being *Mourning Becomes Electra*?

Dying words

a Depending on which source you want to believe, the dying words of which nineteenth-century prime minister were either 'Oh my country, how I leave my country' or 'I think I could eat one of Bellamy's veal pies'?

b Which nineteenth-century prime minister's last words were reputedly 'Die my dear doctor, that's the last thing I shall do'?

c Which statesman said on ascending the scaffold in 1535, 'See me safe up, and for my coming down, let me shift for myself'?

11 YOUR STARTER FOR 10

The Tropic of Capricorn passes through four South American countries: Chile, Brazil, Argentina and which other?

Bridges

a Which bridge, designed and built by Benjamin Baker in the late 1880s, was one of the world's first cantilever bridges and for several years had the world's longest span?

b The collapse of which bridge in the United States in 1940, only four months after its completion, led to modifications in the design of the aerodynamics of the decks of suspension bridges?

c What is the name of the bridge over the Thames at Dartford on the M25, which was opened to traffic in 1991 and is Britain's longest cable-stayed bridge?

12 YOUR STARTER FOR 10

In the Church of England, the diocese of a bishop is a see or bishopric. What name is given to the area of ecclesiastical authority of an archbishop?

BONUS QUESTIONS

Japanese history

a The last holder of which title – an abbreviation of the Japanese for 'barbarian-quelling generalissimo' – was held by the Tokugawa Yoshinobu from 1866 until 1867?

b What was the name of the American naval officer who headed the expedition that, in 1853, entered the harbour at Uraga, which led to the end of Japanese isolation and the eventual fall of the Shogunate?

c Meaning 'way of the warrior', what was the name of the code of conduct for the Samurai class that, in the mid nineteenth century was made the basis of ethical training for the whole of Japanese society?

13 YOUR STARTER FOR 10

What title was given to barristers of at least ten years standing, appointed on the recommendation of the Lord Chancellor to sit in the county court and also hear middle-ranking criminal cases in the crown court?

BONUS QUESTIONS

Joint winners of the Nobel Peace Prize

a Who declined the 1973 Nobel Peace Prize that he was to have shared with Henry Kissinger for their negotiations in trying to resolve the Vietnam conflict?

b Who were jointly awarded the Nobel Peace Prize in 1978 for their efforts to end conflict in the Middle East?

c Who shared the 1993 Peace Prize for 'their work for the peaceful termination of the apartheid regime'?

14 YOUR STARTER FOR 10

What was brought to England by King Edward I in 1296, repossessed by the Scots in 1950, recovered within months, and finally returned to London?

BONUS QUESTIONS

Dictionaries

a Which multi-volume 'dictionary' excludes living persons and was edited from 1882–91 by Virginia Woolf's father, Sir Leslie Stephen?

b In 1828, an alternative to Dr Johnson's dictionary of 1755 was offered by which American?

c Thomas Elyot's 'dictionary' of 1538 was the first major publication of its kind. What type of dictionary was it?

15

YOUR STARTER FOR 10

In which Sumerian city was a great Ziggurat, or step pyramid, constructed about the twenty-second century BC on whose summit was a small shrine, bedchamber of the moon god Nannar (Nan-naar), Patron Deity and Divine King of the City?

BONUS QUESTIONS

Chart-topping songs and the films they come from
a Wet Wet Wet's 'Love Is All Around' is featured in which film?
b Bill Haley and his Comets' 'Rock Around The Clock', which topped the UK singles charts for three weeks in 1955 and again for two weeks in 1956, featured in which Sidney Poitier film?
c Cher's only solo number one single, 'The Shoop Shoop Song (It's In His Kiss)' featured in which film, when she co-starred with Winona Ryder and Bob Hoskins?

16

YOUR STARTER FOR 10

What name was given to the British literary generation that emerged in the 1950s from working-class and lower middle-class origins who shared an outspoken disdain for the British Establishment? Its members included John Braine, Arnold Wesker and John Osborne.

BONUS QUESTIONS

The Three Kings
a The gold shrine to the Three Kings, or Magi, can be seen near the high altar of which German cathedral?
b Off the northern coast of which Commonwealth country can the Three Kings islands be found?
c The three kings of England – who reigned between 924 and 955 – were all the sons of which king?

17

YOUR STARTER FOR 10

The fact that it has so frequently been the scene of European battles since the early eighteenth century has given rise to what nickname for Belgium?

BONUS QUESTIONS

Passes
a The ruins of the Roman fort of Mediobogdum can be found halfway up which Lake District pass?
b The Khyber Pass connects Jalalabad in Afghanistan with which Pakistani city?
c Which two countries are linked by the Brenner Pass?

18 YOUR STARTER FOR 10

The present system of standard time employs 24 meridians of longitude, starting with the prime meridian through Greenwich. How many degrees of longitude are each of these meridians apart?

Quotations

a Which eighteenth-century political propagandist wrote, 'The sublime and the ridiculous are often so nearly related...one step above the sublime, makes the ridiculous; and one step above the ridiculous, makes the sublime again'?

b Which seventeenth-century English poet wrote the following lines? 'Ran on embattled armies clad in iron, and, weaponless himself, made arms ridiculous'?

c In which novel, published in nine volumes between 1760 and 1767, does Uncle Toby say, 'Our armies swore terribly in Flanders, but nothing to this'?

19 YOUR STARTER FOR 10

In the 1960s, New London Bridge was moved to a location in which American state?

Place names

a What is the local spelling of the city known in English as Vienna?

b What is the local spelling of the city known in English as Prague?

c What is the local spelling of the city known in English as Warsaw?

20 YOUR STARTER FOR 10

Which term was first used by German psychologist William Stern, although it was based on a system of measurement devised by Alfred Binet, along with Theodore Simon?

Technical developments in cinema

a Which process, whereby a motion picture is projected on a screen with the width of the image being two and a half times its height, was invented in the late 1920s and first introduced by 20th Century Fox in the 1953 film *The Robe*?

b Which system was evolved in 1974 for the 1975 film *Earthquake* and involved the augmentation of violent action on screen with intense waves of high-decibel sound?

c Which form of large-screen technology was developed in Canada, first shown at Expo '70 in Japan, and provides an image three times bigger than 70 millimetre systems?

SPARE STARTER QUESTIONS

21 Nineteenth-century French scientist Jean Foucault gave what name to a device consisting of a rapidly spinning wheel mounted in a framework that permits it to rotate about any axis?

22 Which city, the capital of Limburg Province in south-eastern Netherlands, gives its name to a treaty agreed in December 1991 by the member states of the European Community?

23 What is being described? Approximately 4.5 inches across, with a transparent plastic coating, the metal beneath this is etched with microscopic pits carrying a digital code. It was introduced to Britain in December 1983?

24 In what way was the birth of Virginia Dare at Roanoke Island on 18 August 1587, the daughter of settlers Ananias and Ellinor Dare, a first in the history of the United States?

25 Which object, measuring just over 14 feet in length and 3½ feet wide, has been in its present location, the cathedral of San Giovanni Battista, since 1578, although its history prior to the fourteenth century has been the subject of much conjecture?

ANSWERS

GAME ONE

1 Toni Morrison
(a) Santiago (33.26 s; Sydney is 34 s). (b) Tokyo (35.41 s.; San Francisco is 37.45 s). (c) Palma de Mallorca (2.38 e.; Algiers is 2.56 e).

2 The Stoic School (Stoicism)
(a) Ethics (b) Baruch Spinoza
(c) Empiricism

3 Monday
(a) Parallelogram (b) Parabola
(c) Trapezium

4 Charlie Chaplin
(a) Staccato (b) Rallentando
(c) Crescendo pedal

5 Six
(a) The site of a regular market.
(b) Place of a church. (c) Stream or spring.

6 Eric Cantona
(a) Carrie Fisher (daughter of Eddie Fisher and Debbie Reynolds, later wife of Paul Simon). (b) Jamie Lee Curtis (daughter of Janet Leigh, murdered in *Psycho*, and Tony Curtis). (c) Melanie Griffith (daughter of Tippi Hedren).

7 *Peter and the Wolf*
(a) 1972 (b) Sir Flinders Petrie
(c) Rameses II

8 The Third Reading
(a) Frans Hals (*The Laughing Cavalier*, 1624, is in the Wallace Collection). (b) Frederic Chopin and George Sand (c) Dedham

9 Waterloo (Wellington, born 1 May 1769; Napoleon, born 15 August 1769).
(a) The sperm whale (b) Sheep's wool (c) Beeswax

10 Pasta
(a) High-level languages (accept problem-oriented languages).
(b) Cobol (common business-oriented language). (c) C

11 The residue (accept residuary estate).
(a) Cedilla (b) Tilde (c) Circumflex

12 100 metres (1924 Paris Olympics)
(a) Pre-molars (b) Dentine
(c) Periodontics

13 Nick Park
(a) Walker Cup (Golf) (b) The William Webb Ellis Trophy (Rugby Union World Cup). (c) FA Cup

14 The movement of a plant (or part of a plant) towards a source of light.
(a) Numbers (Hebrew name is Bemidbar). (b) Esther and Ruth.
(c) First Book of Samuel

15 Mongoose
(a) Henry Bessemer (b) Sulphur
(c) Fischer and Tropsch.

16 Quantum physics
(a) Daniel Quilp (b) Craig Charles
(c) Doc

17 In Xanadu
(a) To allow the passage of a bill
legalizing abortion (as a Roman
Catholic, he did not feel he could
personally agree to the bill, which
was signed by Parliament in the
absence of the monarch). (b) Stanley
Baldwin (c) Queen Wilhelmina

18 Fingerprints
(a) Caldera (b) Mesa (c) Cordillera

19 Action Painting
(a) Buff (b) In Graham Greene's
Brighton Rock. (c) William Howard
Russell

20 Checkmate
(a) Gottfried Leibniz (b) F (accept
Zero F).(c) Rational number
(an integer is a whole number).

21 Anniversary of Her Majesty the
Queen's accession (1952).
22 Aphelion
23 Self-contained underwater breathing
apparatus.
24 Mrs Warren's Profession.
25 Beethoven's Fifth Piano Concerto in
E Flat, opus 73.

GAME TWO
1 George Bernard Shaw
(a) Benjamin Britten (b) Richard
Wagner (c) Hereford, Worcester
and Gloucester.

2 80 (212 - 32 = 180 (Fahrenheit);
100 - 0 = 100 (Celsius). Therefore
the answer is 80.) (a) Guyana (b)
The Republic of Ireland (c) Pakistan

3 Boxgrove Man
(a) Magnificat (b) Tibetan
Buddhists (c) John Irving

4 William Tell
(a) Salisbury (b) Christiaan Huygens
(c) The quartz crystal.

5 Cher (for *Moonstruck*).
(a) Pluperfect (accept past perfect).
(b) Dative (c) Gerund

6 Fauvism (French for wild beast).
(a) (Sir) Roger Bannister
(b) Dr W. G. Grace (c) Sir Arthur
Conan Doyle

7 Mary Robinson
(a) Poundbury (b) Port Sunlight
(c) Robert Owen

8 Velcro
(a) El Salvador (b) Unita
(c) Shining Path (Sendero
Luminoso).

9 Helen of Troy
(a) Soliloquy (b) Tableau
(c) Masque

10 Stagflation
(a) Christian Dior (b) William
Shakespeare (New Place was in
Stratford-upon-Avon). (c) The
cuckoo

11 Andrea Palladio
(a) Longitudinal waves (b) It is
raised by one octave. (c) Decibel

12 Two (23 and 29).
(a) Cardinal Richelieu **(b)** Sir Anthony Van Dyck **(c)** Francis Bacon

13 Ignoble Strife
(a) John Piper **(b)** *Alice in Wonderland* or *Alice's Adventures In Wonderland.* **(c)** Oliver Cromwell

14 Saint Vitus
(a) Ten pin bowling **(b)** Polo **(c)** Table tennis

15 Carbon 14 (has a half life of 5700 years).
(a) Joe 'King' Oliver **(b)** Miles Davis **(c)** Wynton Marsalis

16 Colonel Muammar Al-Quaddafi
(a) Blood pressure **(b)** Systolic and diastolic pressures (the systolic pressure is the high pressure).
(c) (Jan Evangelista) Purkinje

17 Take That
(a) *The Scream* **(b)** The (Soccer) World Cup **(c)** The theft of the *Mona Lisa*.

18 The Four Horsemen of the Apocalypse
(a) Leonidas (I) **(b)** (Marcus Licinius) Crassus **(c)** Xenophon

19 Paul Scott
(a) The history of medicine.
(b) Childhood (toys, dolls, etc.).
(c) The Duke of Wellington

20 Matrix
(a) Bobby Fischer **(b)** Gary Kasparov (he was 22 years old at the time). **(c)** Nigel Short

21 Denis Thatcher
22 'Contrat Social' or 'Social Contract'.
23 Pluto
24 Memphis
25 Mach Number

GAME THREE
1 Colosseum
(a) Anomy **(b)** Nuclear family **(c)** Gemeinschaft (Gemeinschaft is a rural, peasant society, while Gesellschaft is typified by a modern, cosmopolitan society; the concepts were elaborated by German socio-logist Ferdinand Tonnies in *Gemeinschaft und Gesellschaft* (Community and Society) in 1887).

2 Mayor (Attlee, Stepney 1919-20; Eastwood, Carmel, elected 1986; Roberts, elected Mayor of Weatherfield twice, most recently in Spring 1994; Henchard, Mayor of Casterbridge).
(a) Mali **(b)** Lesotho **(c)** Angola

3 Cherry
(a) The Sorbonne **(b)** Massachusetts Institute of Technology **(c)** Columbia

4 Neanderthal
(a) *Rosencrantz and Guildenstern are Dead* (by Tom Stoppard; char-acters from Hamlet). **(b)** *King Lear* **(c)** *The Lady Macbeth Of Mtsenk District* (by Shostakovich; the title reverted to its original name, *Katerina Ismailova;* apparently the opera was described as 'chaos instead of music' and 'a leftist mess instead of human music').

5 *The Second Sex*
  (a) John Maynard Keynes
  (b) E. F. Schumacher (c) (Von)
  Hayek

6 Tracy Edwards
  (a) Mormons (b) Christian Science
  (founded by Mary Baker Eddy and
  believing that as God is good and is
  spirit, matter and evil are not real).
  (c) Billy Graham

7 Kilimanjaro
  (a) John Grierson (*The Night Mail*
  is probably his most famous film).
  (b) Cinema verité (François
  Truffaut's 1959 film *Les Quatre
  Cent Coups* demonstrates this technique). (c) A film that appears to be
  a fictional work, but is in fact based
  on a true story and real people
  (*Citizen Kane* is an example, Kane
  being William Randolf Hearst).

8 Harold Wilson
  (a) 1900 (Salisbury dissolved
  Parliament and called a snap election in an attempt to profit from
  recent Boer war successes).
  (b) Approved candidates for the
  Liberal/Conservative alliance were
  endorsed by a letter (or coupon)
  signed by Lloyd George.
  (c) Countess Constance Markievicz
  (a Sinn Fein candidate, who never
  took her seat as she was still in
  prison when elected, for her part in
  the 1916 Easter rising in Dublin;
  Lady Astor was elected in 1919 and
  became the first woman to take a
  seat in Parliament).

9 Chaos Theory (Lorenz originally
  used the image of a seagull).

(a) The Magic Flute (in the opera so
entitled by Mozart; first performed
in Vienna in October 1791, two
months before the composer's death).
(b) Carmen (in Bizet's opera of that
name). (The heroine is stabbed by
Don Jose -- she rejected him in favour
of Escamillo, a bull-fighter.) (c)
Turandot. ('Nessun Dorma'.)

10 'Lucy In The Sky With Diamonds'
   (it was not released as a single by
   The Beatles, but, in November 1974,
   it reached number 10 in the British
   charts for Elton John and number 1
   in the USA in 1975).
   (a) Congress Poland (also called
   Congress Kingdom of Poland, ruled
   by Tsars from 1815 until its loss in
   the First World War). (b) The Black
   Sea (c) Berlin Congress, 1878.

11 Switzerland
   (a) The Urals (b) The Karakorams
   (c) The Pyrénées

12 Regis
   (a) Osteopathy (a system of healing
   based on the manipulation of bones
   or muscle from the Greek words
   'osteon', meaning 'bone', and
   'potheia', meaning suffering).
   (b) The feet. (c) Homoeopathy

13 Pointillist/pointillism (Seurat is
   probably the best-known pointillist
   painter and Webern is particularly
   noted for pointillism in music).
   (a) Vivien (accept Nimue [nimoo-ay]
   or Nimiane [nimmi-aan]) (b) 25
   March (commemorating the Annun-
   ciation of the Virgin Mary).
   (c) Canada

14 *Decline and Fall*
   (a) James Whistler (the attack was on his painting *Nocturne in Black and Gold: the falling rocket*). **(b)** Socrates **(c)** Alfred Dreyfus

15 Eight
   (a) Anna Karenina. **(b)** Tess of the D'Urbervilles (accept Tess/Teresa Durbyfield – heroine's real name). **(c)** Madame Bovary

16 On Bank of England bank notes (on the £5 note, Stephenson superseded Wellington; on the £20 note, Faraday succeeded Shakespeare; on the £50 note, Sir John Houblon, the Bank of England's first governor, replaced Wren).
   (a) FA Cup **(b)** Berwick Rangers **(c)** Alex Ferguson (Manchester United, 1990-91; Aberdeen, 1982-3).

17 *The Comedy of Errors*
   (a) *Hymenoptera* **(b)** A bird. **(c)** *The Tempest* (sung by Ariel, Act V, Scene1).

18 Quota
   (a) Consul (Rome's last king was Tarquin the Proud or, in Latin, Tarquinius Superbus).
   (b) Cicero **(c)** Mark Antony, Lepidus and Octavian (later Emperor Augustus).

19 A double duck (a duck in each innings of a match – not used very often these days).
   (a) Marie Rambert (Ballet Rambert was renamed the Rambert Dance Company in 1987). **(b)** Sir Kenneth Macmillan **(c)** Margot Fonteyn

and Rudolf Nureyev.

20 Speed of light (in free space/in a vacuum).
   (a) Five (the USA, Russia, the UK, France and China). **(b)** Fifteen (the other ten are elected for two-year periods). **(c)** Taiwan (formerly Formosa; expelled when Communist China was admitted).

21 Cardinal Richelieu (1585–1642; he was the Chief Minister to Louis XIII from 1624–42, and his Secretary, Père Joseph, was the original 'Grey Eminence').
22 CND (Campaign for Nuclear Disarmament).
23 Gebbard Von Blücher
24 Soy sauce
25 Kidney

GAME FOUR
1 Superman
   (a) Dr Hastings Banda (of Malawi) **(b)** Ho Chi Minh (North Vietnam) **(c)** Chaim Weizmann (Israel)

2 Iceland
   (a) Alexander Selkirk **(b)** Henry Hudson **(c)** Malta

3 Vector
   (a) *Manhattan* **(b)** Ralph Vaughan Williams **(c)** *Out of Africa*

4 Qattara Depression
   (a) Tipperary **(b)** Sussex **(c)** Lathes

5 A Grecian urn.
   (a) Spassky (Chess Champions). **(b)** Austin (all Poets Laureate). **(c)** Wojtyla (Popes).

6 Holography
   (a) Body louse (b) Bilharziasis (or
   schistosomiasis). (c) Tsetse fly

7 Kurt Cobain
   (a) *The Plumed Serpent* (b) Vacuum
   cleaner salesman (c) Gabriel Garcia
   Marquez

8 Wisconsin
   (a) Spanish Civil War (b) *All Quiet
   on the Western Front* (c) American
   Civil War

9 Hats off, strangers
   (a) Stipendiary magistrate (b) Rider
   (c) Power of attorney

10 *Mein Kampf*
    (a) Simon Le Bon (b) Billy Joel
    (c) Bruce Dickinson

11 1032 (a kilobyte is 2 to the power
    of 10 bytes and there are 8 bits in a
    byte).
    (a) They were popes. (b) On a
    football pools coupon (Australian).
    (c) They are months in the Jewish
    calendar.

12 St James (of Compostela or The
    Great)
    (a) Poll tax (b) Windows
    (c) SET (Selective Employment Tax).

13 D
    (a) REM (Rapid Eye Movement).
    (b) Martin Fry (c) Tammy Wynette

14 Margarine
    (a) Jainism (b) Zoroastrianism
    (c) Rastafarianism

15 Queen Victoria

(a) Honolulu (Hawaii)
(b) Kuala Lumpur (Malaysia)
(c) Dar-es-Salaam (Tanzania)

16 Helsinki
    (a) Anther (b) Stigma (c) Sepals

17 19 (3 + 7 + 9)
    (a) 6 (b) 36 (c) 12

18 Howitzer
    (a) Stephane Mallarmé (b) Bull-
    fighting (c) The Kinks

19 Renoir
    (a) Fifth Monarchy Men
    (b) Austerlitz (c) The Seven Sisters

20 Opening of the Summer Olympic
    Games
    (a) Bombay (b) *A Passage to India*
    (c) *The Jewel in the Crown*

21 Winchester
22 Magellan (Magellanic clouds)
23 Dandelion
24 Okapi
25 Lysander

GAME FIVE

1 Capillarity or capillary action.
   (a) Sioux (specifically Hunkpapa
   Sioux). (b) Navajo (c) Cherokee

2 Damascus (Damson, Damask,
   Damascene and Damask Rose).
   (a) Thomas Hobbes (b) Jeremy
   Bentham (c) John Stuart Mill

3 Odessa
   (a) Henry II (b) 'Planta' is Latin for
   plant, 'genista' is Latin for broom, of
   which Henry's father Geoffrey of
   Anjou used to wear a sprig or

possibly used to plant to improve his hunting cover. **(c)** Prime Minister

4 Velocity
(a) Alfred Dreyfus **(b)** Robert Falcon Scott (accept Scott of the Antarctic). **(c)** Sarajevo (the book is entitled *Zlata's Diary*).

5 Goalkeeper
(a) Enrico Caruso **(b)** Beniamino Gigli **(c)** Luciano Pavarotti

6 Chicken
(a) Romansch (accept Grishun or Grisons). **(b)** Basque **(c)** Maltese

7 Phrenology
(a) Cyprus **(b)** Minorca **(c)** Corfu

8 Devon Malcolm
(a) Bath and Wells (1987-91).
(b) Durham and Winchester (bishops not archbishops, so Canterbury and York are not correct!) **(c)** The Bishop of Sodor and Man (The Isle of Man has its own Parliament).

9 Eight
(a) Cuckoo **(b)** Charles II **(c)** Falcon

10 Alexandria
(a) It is the theme music for *The Archers*. **(b)** Iago (*Othello*, Act 3, Scene 3). **(c)** It was introduced into England by Sir William Gage.

11 From the old English 'lik', meaning 'a body'. (The gate provided shelter for the coffin and mourners before the funeral service.)
(a) Stanley Baldwin **(b)** Alec Douglas-Home **(c)** Henry Campbell Bannerman

12 Ernesto 'Che' Guevara
(a) St Thomas More **(b)** Edward the Confessor **(c)** St Laurence (accept also St Laurentius [of Canterbury]).

13 The Land of Nod
(a) The Scapegoat **(b)** Dante Gabriel Rossetti **(c)** Sir Walter Raleigh

14 Winds
(a) *Wuthering Heights* **(b)** *Clarissa* **(c)** *The Prime of Miss Jean Brodie*

15 The Louvre
(a) The Family Division (was the Probate, Divorce and Admiralty Division until 1970). **(b)** Civil and Criminal. **(c)** Injunction

16 Namibia
(a) Ely **(b)** Westminster Cathedral **(c)** Liverpool Metropolitan (or Roman Catholic) Cathedral

17 Nouvelle Cuisine
(a) The anniversary of the death of Alfred Nobel. **(b)** If the Prize has been withheld in the previous year. **(c)** Economic science (economics).

18 Carlos/The Jackal
(a) The Titans **(b)** Gog and Magog (in early medieval times, they were known as Gogmagog). **(c)** François Rabelais

19 Bill Wyman
(a) Shoddy **(b)** Worsted **(c)** Tulle

20 Lateral thinking
(a) Specifically just before and just after a total eclipse of the sun (accept eclipse).**(b)** Transit **(c)** Johannes Kepler

21 Think tank
22 Carboniferous
23 Peterborough
24 Henry III
25 Dadaism

GAME SIX

1 Milwaukee
   (a) Clocks and watches **(b)** Guns
   (c) Play chess.

2 Mary II and Anne (Anne Hyde
   was the first wife of James II).
   (a) Venus **(b)** Albedo (Latin word is
   'albens'). **(c)** Uranus

3 Nicotine (Jacques Nicot).
   (a) Ice hockey (The Stanley Cup).
   (b) The AFC (American Football
   Conference) and NFC (National
   Football Conference). **(c)** Croatia

4 *Carmen* (the musical was *Carmen
   Jones).*
   (a) Argentina and Chile **(b)** Easter
   Island **(c)** Kensington Gardens

5 The Bauhaus
   (a) MGM film studios (Ars Gratia
   Artis). **(b)** The Most Honourable
   Order of the Bath **(c)** Citius, Altius,
   Fortius (Faster, Higher, Stronger).

6 Brecon Beacons
   (a) For supporting their two sons in
   revolt against him (the future
   Richard I and John). **(b)** James
   Hepburn, fourth Earl of Bothwell
   (c) Mrs (Maria) Fitzherbert

7 Giant Panda
   (a) Yew **(b)** The elder **(c)** Worcester
   (he hid in an oak tree at Boscobel
   House, Shropshire, in 1651).

8 *Middlemarch* (by George Eliot).
   (a) Myalgic encephalomyelitis
   (b) In vitro fertilization (literally
   meaning 'fertilization in glass').
   (c) Repetitive strain injury (accept
   repetition strain injury or repetitive
   stress injury).

9 Mantilla
   (a) Ecuador **(b)** Greece **(c)** Interpol
   (International Criminal Police
   Organization).

10 Antimony (stibnite is a combination of antimony and sulphur).
   (a) Thomas Carlyle **(b)** Henry James
   (c) Virginia Woolf

11 The Father of the House
   (a) The Barents Sea (after Willem
   Barents). **(b)** The Ross Sea (in
   Antarctica, after Sir James Clark
   Ross). **(c)** The Bering Sea (after Vitus
   Johansen Bering).

12 *The Light of the World*
   (a) Vikram Seth (the book is *A
   Suitable Boy)* **(b)** Hong Kong
   (c) *The Remains of the Day* (by
   Kazuo Ishiguro)

13 The Praetorian Guard
   (a) Precambrian (from about 4600
   million years ago, to about 600
   million years ago). **(b)** Cretaceous
   period (the Cretaceous comes after
   the Jurassic). **(c)** Holocene epoch

14 *When Harry Met Sally*
   (a) Helston **(b)** Josephine Baker
   (c) Salome (who danced 'The Dance
   of the Seven Veils').

15 The bribing or attempted bribery of a jury or juror.
(a) Lohengrin (b) Homer (who reputedly lived on the banks of the river Meander). (c) Ben Johnson

16 Bulgaria
(a) Virginia (b) William Harrison (c) F. D. Roosevelt

17 North Sea oil fields.
(a) It would be shown full face (with its face turned towards the beholder). (b) It would be running (also accept 'with right foot raised'). (c) Bringing together the arms of several families in one escutcheon.

18 The Miles Davis Quintet
(a) Evening Star (built Swindon 1960, in service for exactly 5 years, withdrawn March 1965 but not broken up and could be brought back into service). (b) AMTRAK (c) Japan (between Honshū and Hokkaidō).

19 *The Rubaiyat of Omar Khayyam*
(a) Julius Caesar (b) Sherlock Holmes (c) Henry VIII

20 Solenoid
(a) The owl and the pussycat.
(b) Dick Whittington (c) The Duke and Duchess of Windsor.

21 The Glyndebourne
22 Pharmacopoeia
23 *Exxon Valdez*
24 List processing or list processor
25 Court of St James

GAME SEVEN
1   115 (they are wedding anniver-saries: 25 + 40 + 50 = 115).
(a) Jigsaw puzzles (b) Austerlitz
(c) 'Biography is about chaps.'

2   They are all subjects of Elgar's *Enigma Variations*.
(a) Top Cat (b) Penelope Pitstop
(c) Captain Pugwash

3   International Style
(a) The Crystal Palace. (b) Newgate Prison (c) Temple Bar

4   8 (1, 3, 4, 5, 6 and 7 would be dismissed in the first over, with 2, 9, 10 and 11 in the second, leaving 8 stranded at the other end).
(a) Linear B (Linear A is still undeci-phered). (b) Etruscan. (c) Gothic.

5   Lettuce (the Latin for milk is 'lactis').
(a) Florence Nightingale
(b) J. M. Barrie. (c) T. S. Eliot.

6   U2
(a) Cowpox (b) Tuberculosis (accept consumption). (c) Albert Sabin (Jonas Salk also developed a vaccine against polio, but his was injected by needle and the orally administered vaccine, normally given on a lump of sugar, proved more popular).

7   James I
(a) Kurt Weill (*The Threepenny Opera*). (b) Stephen Sondheim
(c) Elton John and Bernie Taupin.

8   Tin miners
(a) Judas Iscariot (b) Louisiana Purchase (c) The Duchy of Cornwall (in effect, the Prince of Wales).

9 A general election.
(a) The red telephone kiosk.
(b) Peccavi (I have sinned).
(c) The attempted assassination of Hitler by German army officers.

10 Clive James
(a) Chile (b) Richard Cromwell
(c) Egypt

11 Rainbow
(a) Pierre Corneille (b) Jean-Baptiste Racine. (c) Molière

12 *Carpe diem*
(a) Numbered shirts. (b) Starting stalls. (c) Fosbury Flop

13 Existentialism
(a) Worcester (b) Edward II
(c) Windsor (St George's Chapel).

14 Prague (the numbers are those of Mozart's symphonies).
(a) '...Give me liberty or give me death.' (b) '...Never had it so good.'
(c) 'Annus Horribilis.'

15 Colourings
(a) The Canary Islands (b) French Guiana (c) Pitcairn Island

16 *Brave New World* by Aldous Huxley.
(a) George Boole (b) Kurt Godel
(c) Alan Turing

17 Harvard
(a) Kabuki (b) Tea (c) Haiku (accept Hokku).

18 He made the first supersonic flight (accept he broke the sound barrier).
(a) Geoffrey Howe (b) Alex Salmond (c) Norman Fowler

19 Slough
(a) Prime minister (b) Thomas Seymour (c) Attorney general

20 *The Arabian Nights*
(a) St Pancras (b) Agincourt (1415)
(c) St Louis

21 Chromosome
22 Neptune
23 Sierra
24 Lady Chatterley
25 Salmon

GAME EIGHT

1 Coptic Christians or Copts.
(a) Giotto (b) Van Dyck
(c) (Michelangelo) Caravaggio

2 Bannockburn
(a) Harold Holt (b) Gough Whitlam
(c) Bob Hawke

3 Darby and Joan
(a) Acids (b) The pH scale (c) Buffer solution

4 Hyperion
(a) The Cottesloe (b) The Old Vic
(c) Peter Hall

5 James Stirling
(a) Portugal (b) South Korea
(c) India

6 Dynamics
(a) Persepolis (former capital of the Persian Empire). (b) The Western (or Wailing) Wall. (c) Eleanor Crosses

7 Six (pi = approximately 3.14, E = approximately 2.72).
(a) Printer (b) A bookseller
(c) Alexander Borodin

8 The Samaritans
   (a) Hyacinthus **(b)** Galatea **(c)** He was torn to pieces by his own hounds.

9 Spaghetti Junction
   (a) Clarence Birdseye **(b)** Fluorine **(c)** Chlorine

10 William Wordsworth
   (a) The Fronde **(b)** Jacobins or Jacobin Club. **(c)** Commune (or Communards).

11 Jim Bergerac
   (a) Kodiak Bear **(b)** Polar Bear **(c)** Winnie the Pooh

12 Kibbutzim
   (a) It refers to Adam and Eve making themselves breeches. **(b)** Authorized version or King James Bible. **(c)** The Good News Bible

13 The Stock Exchange (stags and bears: stags apply for new share issues with a view to selling at once at a profit; bears unload shares in a falling market).
   (a) Coventry Cathedral **(b)** Falstaff **(c)** Handel's *Messiah*

14 Baud (after M. E. Baudot).
   (a) John Clare **(b)** The Ettrick Shepherd **(c)** Alexander Pope

15 A woman.
   (a) Oslo **(b)** Pretoria (South Africa) **(c)** Santiago (in Chile).

16 Sans serif (means 'without elaboration').
   (a) Simon Bolivar **(b)** Bernardo O'Higgins **(c)** General Manuel Belgrano (sinking of the *General Belgrano* during the Falklands War).

17 Alexander Solzhenitsyn
   (a) Factorial (e.g., 5! = 1 x 2 x 3 x 4 x 5 = 120). **(b)** Surd (e.g., square root of 3). **(c)** Googol

18 Mr David Blunkett's guide dog.
   (a) Walter and John Huston (*Treasure of the Sierra Madre*). **(b)** Ford Madox (Ford Madox Ford and Ford Madox Brown respectively). **(c)** Henry and Washington Irving.

19 Conservatory (from 'conservatorio', the orphans being known as conservati).
   (a) (Ottorino) Respighi **(b)** (Gian Lorenzo) Bernini **(c)** Trevi Fountain

20 Winning the Derby (names of horses, not jockeys).
   (a) George III **(b)** Mrs Freeman **(c)** Benjamin Franklin

21 Bismuth
22 Punjab (Panj = five, Ab = water).
23 A. E. Houseman
24 *Drop The Dead Donkey*
25 Jupiter

GAME NINE
1 Alan Clark
   (a) Malmaison **(b)** The Loire **(c)** Marcel Pagnol

2 Tanzania
   (a) *Samuel Pepys' Diaries* **(b)** Rosetta Stone **(c)** Beatrix Potter

3 Emery
   (a) Kansas **(b)** New Hampshire

(c) Arkansas

4 *Naked Gun*
(a) (Thermonuclear) fusion (accept conversion of hydrogen into helium, but fission is wrong – it's the splitting *apart* of nuclei; fusion is the joining *together* of nuclei.) **(b)** Photosphere (accept light sphere).
(c) It takes 8 minutes (or, more precisely, 8 minutes and 20 seconds).

5 Romeo
(a) Dame Clara Butt **(b)** Sir Peter Pears **(c)** Dame Joan Sutherland

6 Stephen Fry (his first was *The Liar* in 1991).
(a) The crossing of the English Channel. **(b)** It was man-powered/pedal-powered.
(c) The first without refuelling.

7 Gallbladder
(a) Claude Lorraine **(b)** Caravaggio **(c)** Tintoretto

8 Austria and Prussia.
(a) They were used for 'bumping' – hammering the table after a toast.
(b) Dorothy Parker ('Men seldom make passes At girls who wear glasses'). **(c)** Used motor cars.

9 Fork
(a) Sir Walter Raleigh **(b)** Emmeline Pankhurst **(c)** Theory of evolution (accept Darwin's theory).

10 Fog (mist and smog not acceptable with this definition).
(a) *The Downing Street Years* **(b)** Hugo Young **(c)** Ronald Reagan

11 Nelson's Column
(a) Geotropism **(b)** Radicle **(c)** Rhizome

12 Ku Klux Klan
(a) Book of Revelation or Revelation to John or Revelation of St John the Divine. **(b)** *Heart of Darkness* (by Joseph Conrad). **(c)** Vincente Blasco Ibanez

13 Mad cow disease
(a) (King) Stephen **(b)** Roland **(c)** Louis Napoleon or Napoleon III.

14 *Animal Farm* (George Orwell, 1945).
(a) Aida **(b)** (Floria) Tosca **(c)** Lulu

15 Fifth (they have the same rhythm as the Morse Code for V, for victory – dot, dot, dot, dash – and were played after the code sign).
(a) Elizabeth I **(b)** Charles II **(c)** Henry VIII

16 Claude Monet
(a) The Coromandel Coast
(b) The Barbary Coast **(c)** Sardinia

17 They all succeeded their brothers to the throne.
(a) Hexameter **(b)** Sir Thomas Wyatt **(c)** Blank verse

18 Black Sea
(a) Ronnie Scott **(b)** The Marylebone Cricket Club (MCC) **(c)** The Pickwick Club

19 Ignis fatuus
(a) The coroner **(b)** King John **(c)** The Mildenhall Treasure (accept Mildenhall Hoard).

20 Sir Garfield (Gary) Sobers.
   (a) Ambrose Bierce **(b)** Dr Samuel
   Johnson **(c)** The Brothers Grimm

21 Jacques Cartier
22 *The Wizard of Oz*
23 Cartoon
24 Hormones
25 Signing of the Magna Carta.

GAME TEN

1 Analysis of the nature, origin and
   evolution of human settlements.
   (a) Macduff (*Macbeth*, Act V, Scene
   viii). **(b)** Gloucester, afterwards
   Richard III (*Richard III*, Act I, Scene
   iii). **(c)** Juliet (*Romeo and Juliet*, Act
   I, Scene iii).

2 Alfred, Lord Tennyson
   (a) Battle Above the Clouds **(b)** La
   Rochelle **(c)** Otterburn

3 Beethoven's 'Les Adieux' Piano
   Sonata, No. 26, opus 81a.
   (a) Amedeo Modigliani **(b)** Joe
   Orton **(c)** Fred Archer (champion
   jockey).

4 Macau
   (a) Croatia **(b)** Lithuania **(c)** Belarus
   (byellaroos).

5 Kaolin
   (a) Amritsar **(b)** The Taj Mahal
   (c) Ellora

6 Chihuahua
   (a) Lactic acid **(b)** Everything smells
   unpleasant. **(c)** Cruciate ligaments

7 Mayerling
   (a) Protagonist **(b)** Deus ex Machina
   (c) Orchestra

8 René Descartes
   (a) Ian Smith **(b)** *Fram*
   (c) Auckland, New Zealand

9 Cyprus (independence was achieved
   in 1960).
   (a) The time it takes for the sun to
   return to the same position among
   the stars. **(b)** Taurus **(c)** Tycho Brahe
   (Two-co Braar).

10 The Famous Five
   (a) Mercury **(b)** Bauxite **(c)** Galena
   (also known as lead glance).

11 Thug
   (a) Richard I **(b)** George I
   (c) Edward VII

12 Quadratic equation
   (a) Sleipnir **(b)** She stumbled over a
   molehill, throwing her mount.
   (c) Bring the good news from Ghent.

13 The swearing-in of Nelson
   Mandela as South African President.
   (a) Winston Churchill **(b)** Denis
   Healey **(c)** Deputy Chief Whip

14 Silvio Berlusconi
   (a) 'The clocks were striking
   thirteen.' **(b)** *Jane Eyre* **(c)** 'We have
   no time to stand and stare.'

15 Highgate
   (a) Carl Gustav Jung **(b)** Standard
   ink blot shapes. **(c)** Parapsychology

16 Lyre-bird (its Latin name is
   Menura, and there are two species:
   Menura superba and *Menura
   alberti*).
   (a) Sergeant Troy (in *Far from the
   Madding Crowd* by Thomas Hardy;

Troy was shot by Farmer Boldwood, his wife is Bathsheba Everdene and the servant is Fanny Robbin). **(b)** John Stonehouse **(c)** Brian Jones (of The Rolling Stones).

17 Asterix the Gaul
 (a) Heracleitus **(b)** John Philip Sousa **(c)** Andrew Jackson

18 The Royal Mile
 (a) Walter Christaller **(b)** The Black Forest **(c)** Cuxhaven

19 Triangulation
 (a) Chartreuse **(b)** (Girolamo) Savonarola **(c)** Trappists

20 Frederick Forsyth
 (a) Maputo **(b)** Ekaterinburg **(c)** Upper Volta

21 Lizard Point (westernmost, northernmost, easternmost and southernmost points).
22 'Little Miss Muffet'
23 Wimbledon Common (Orinoco, Tobermory, and Great Uncle Bulgaria are Wombles).
24 Steven Spielberg
25 The planet Uranus (92 is the atomic number for uranium, named in 1789 after the then newly discovered planet Uranus, 38 is the atomic number for strontium, named after the Scottish village, and 72 is the atomic number for hafnium, the classical name for Copenhagen).

GAME ELEVEN
1 The Channel Tunnel
 (a) Javert **(b)** Sam Spade **(c)** (Eddie) Shoestring

2 Filibuster (or filibustering).
 (a) Anastasia **(b)** Strode **(c)** Zeppo

3 Thomas Huxley
 (a) Tuesdays and Thursdays (starting at 3.15 pm). **(b)** (Drawn) swords **(c)** (Sit down and) put on a hat.

4 Gordonstoun
 (a) President Reagan **(b)** Bruce Springsteen **(c)** *High Society*

5 The Wigmore Hall
 (a) China **(b)** Algeria **(c)** Brazil

6 *The Playboy of the Western World*
 (a) (The skull of) Piltdown Man **(b)** The Zinoviev Letter **(c)** Hans Van Meegeren

7 The Derby
 (a) Lolita **(b)** *Pamela* **(c)** Rebecca

8 Hampton Court
 (a) The Princess Royal (Princess Anne) **(b)** Paul Young **(c)** JFK Stadium

9 Simplon Pass
 (a) The abdication speach of Edward VIII. **(b)** Spiro Agnew **(c)** Charles de Gaulle

10 All letters are in lower case.
 (a) Topaz **(b)** Sapphire **(c)** Jet

11 Helios (the sun God).
 (a) Pantograph **(b)** Theodolite **(c)** Octant

12 Deathwatch beetle
 (a) Oxbow lake **(b)** Erie and Ontario **(c)** Stickle Tarn

13 Neil Kinnock
   (a) (Daniel) Bernoulli (principle that gives aircraft lift). **(b)** Paul Klee **(c)** Arthur Honegger

14 Cameo
   (a) Bad money drives out good.
   (b) To help pay the costs of the civil war. **(c)** Ramsay Macdonald

15 Siegfried
   (a) He was the only recipient of the Victoria Cross (awarded in 1969).
   (b) Wilfred Owen **(c)** For gallantry.

16 Orrery
   (a) Alexander Pushkin **(b)** Nikolai Gogol **(c)** Maxim Gorky

17 Mexico City
   (a) First transpacific flight **(b)** Pan American **(c)** Boeing 747

18 Marlon Brando
   (a) Dotheboys Hall **(b)** *Goodbye Mr Chips* **(c)** Bash Street School

19 Valéry Giscard D'Estaing
   (a) Brazil **(b)** (Black) Swan **(c)** A (red) hand

20 Buddhism
   (a) George Wallace **(b)** Socialist **(c)** Ross Perot

21 *Middlemarch*
22 Cosecant
23 David Bowie
24 English and Latin
25 Talcum powder

GAME TWELVE

1 Colonel Oliver North
   (a) Dorset **(b)** Royal Tunbridge Wells **(c)** Victoria

2 Archbishop of Canterbury
   (a) Saatchi and Saatchi. **(b)** Jack and Bobby Charlton were in England's World Cup-winning side at Wembley. **(c)** Stephen Knight

3 Wellington (New Zealand)
   (a) Brasilia **(b)** Buckminster **(c)** New Delhi (accept Delhi).

4 Alan Paton
   (a) Sales of military equipment to Iraq (accept similar). **(b)** Lord Scarman **(c)** The Profumo Affair

5 Ultraviolet
   (a) Three Choirs Festival **(b)** *Turandot* **(c)** *The Rite of Spring*

6 The Haka
   (a) *Emmerdale* **(b)** *I'm Sorry, I Haven't a Clue* **(c)** Gloria Swanson

7 Peter the Great or Peter I.
   (a) Saint Peter **(b)** Paul Gauguin **(c)** The riddle of the Sphinx.

8 Ludwig Wittgenstein
   (a) Benazir Bhutto **(b)** Bangladesh **(c)** Corazon ('Cory') Aquino

9 Trivia
   (a) Peenemünde **(b)** Cape Kennedy **(c)** Baionur (accept Tyuratam).

10 Handel
   (a) Mars **(b)** Mount Maxwell (after James Maxwell). **(c)** Uganda

11 Hungarian
(a) Catherine de Medici (b) Henry
Hunt (c) They were dressed as
policemen.

12 Medusa
(a) 'Seven swans a-swimming.'
(b) 'And the running of the deer.'
(c) 'We Three Kings' (of Orient are).

13 Endomorphy
(a) Ramadhan (b) Salat (sa-laa-t)
(c) Holy war

14 Oliver Cromwell
(a) Belgravia (b) Le Corbusier
(c) Washington DC

15 *Hedd Wyn*
(a) V (b) C (c) H

16 Puerto Rico
(a) Ovid (b) Catullus (c) Horace

17 DDT
(a) John Bull's other island.
(b) Crete (c) Hispaniola (in the
Greater Antilles).

18 Attorney General
(a) Silkworms (b) Willow pattern
(c) Jade

19 *The Winter's Tale*
(a) *The Naked Maja* (b) *The Birth of
Venus* (c) *Le Déjeuner sur l'Herbe*

20 The length of the overhang of
cloth below the knees.
(a) The Bear and Staff (b) Mistress
Quickly (c) Dr Johnson

21 Francis Bacon
22 Guatemala or Belize

23 John Monks
24 Migraine
25 Frieze

GAME THIRTEEN

1 Nelson Mandela
(a) Bacon (Roger, Francis and
Francis). (b) Hardy (Thomas
Masterman, Thomas and Oliver).
(c) Fry (Elizabeth, Christopher and
Stephen).

2 Carmina Burana
(a) Couscous (b) Polenta
(c) Hominy

3 Pairing
(a) Wagner (b) Stravinsky
(c) Vaughan Williams

4 Epiphytes
(a) Cardinals (b) Conclave (c) Dutch

5 *Blithe Spirit*
(a) Cloud chamber (b) Ronald
Reagan (c) Anthony Burgess

6 Manchu or Ch'ing
(a) The Great Trek (b) Paul Kruger
(c) (Sir Leander Starr) Jameson

7 NATO
(a) Assay (b) Leopard (c) Touchstone

8 Rugby League
(a) By 'The Iron Curtain'.
(b) Haydn's symphonies. (c) The
Pony Express

9 Armature
(a) The Alhambra (b) Windsor
(c) Osborne House

10 From the Greek word 'psephos',

meaning 'pebble' (in ancient Greece, votes were cast by placing a pebble in an urn).
(a) Gideons International **(b)** The Howard League **(c)** Bruce Kent

11 They were awarded the Nobel Prize for Literature in those years.
(a) Shropshire **(b)** Norfolk (not to be confused with Holcombe Court, a Tudor mansion in Devon). **(c)** Castle Drogo (built between 1910 and 1930).

12 Pitch
(a) Beatrix Potter **(b)** Alfred Wainwright **(c)** Ulverston

13 Daleks
(a) One Thousand Guineas or The Oaks. **(b)** Phar Lap **(c)** Eighteen

14 Six
(a) Blore Heath **(b)** Towton **(c)** Flodden

15 Mayan
(a) On the nose. **(b)** Watergate **(c)** Dog days

16 Palindrome
(a) Petra **(b)** Bordeaux **(c)** Ottawa

17 Richard Nixon
(a) The Chief Whip in the Commons. **(b)** The Deputy Speaker **(c)** A former Prime Minister

18 Alfred, Lord Tennyson
(a) Brindisi **(b)** Barcarolle **(c)** Wiegenlied

19 D'Oyly Carte
(a) *The Railway Children* **(b)** Uncle Remus **(c)** *Charlie and the Great Glass Elevator*

20 Société Anonyme
(a) An eagle dropped a tortoise on his head. **(b)** He was struck on the head by a cricket ball. **(c)** Isadora Duncan

21 Pink Noise
22 Virago Press
23 Bell, book and candle.
24 Delft
25 Marsh gas

GAME FOURTEEN

1 The pursuer (the defendant is the defender in Scotland).
(a) Grand Coulee Dam **(b)** Pergau Dam **(c)** Turkey (Iraq and Syria objected to interruption of flow).

2 Serendipity
(a) By talking with pebbles in his mouth or by reciting verses when running or out of breath. **(b)** To look for an honest man. **(c)** Epicurus

3 Became extinct.
(a) Rock particles being transported (by river or sea) are reduced in size as they strike one another or the surrounding channel. (Accept also reduction in size of rock particles due to movement caused by wind.) **(b)** By the joining up of a stalactite and a stalagmite or by the joining up of calcium carbonate (or calcite) deposits on the cave floor and ceiling. **(c)** Arête

4 Holy Roman Emperor
(a) Rights issue **(b)** Qualification share **(c)** Prospectus

5 Andy Warhol
(a) GCHQ **(b)** Clive Ponting
(c) Westland affair (the ministers
were Brittan and Heseltine).

6 *Star Trek*
(a) Lesser Sunda Islands **(b)**
Monkeys (Ramayana) **(c)** Vishnu (in
his dwarf avatar – Brahman).

7 P (pink as these are values of snooker
balls).
(a) Jean Sibelius **(b)** Gioacchino
Rossini **(c)** Giuseppe Verdi (the
comic opera was *Falstaff*).

8 Barbara Castle
(a) Gauleiter **(b)** Emir **(c)** Bey

9 *Wall Street Journal*
(a) Charlie Chaplin **(b)** P. G.
Wodehouse **(c)** Sir Bobby Charlton

10 Eugene O'Neill
(a) William Pitt (the Younger)
(b) Palmerston **(c)** Sir Thomas More

11 Paraguay
(a) Forth (railway) bridge **(b)**
Tacoma Narrows **(c)** Queen
Elizabeth II (span of 450 metres).

12 A province.
(a) Shogun (accept Bakufu).
(b) Matthew Perry **(c)** Bushido

13 Circuit judge
(a) Le Duc Tho **(b)** Anwar Sadat
(Egypt) and Menachem Begin
(Israel). **(c)** President de Klerk (of
South Africa) and Nelson Mandela
(leader of the ANC).

14 Stone of Scone or Stone of Destiny.
(a) *Dictionary of National
Biography* **(b)** Noah Webster
(*American Dictionary of the English
Language*) **(c)** Latin - English

15 Ur
(a) *Four Weddings and a Funeral*
(b) *Blackboard Jungle* **(c)** *Mermaids*

16 Angry Young Men
(a) Cologne **(b)** New Zealand
(c) Edward the Elder

17 The cockpit of Europe.
(a) Hardknott **(b)** Peshawar
(c) Italy and Austria

18 Fifteen degrees (there are 24
meridians, starting from Greenwich,
which is 0 degrees).
(a) Thomas Paine **(b)** John Milton
(c) *Tristram Shandy*

19 Arizona
(a) Wien **(b)** Praha (Pra-ha)
(c) Warszawa

20 IQ or intelligence quotient.
(a) Cinemascope **(b)** Sensurround
(c) Imax

21 Gyroscope
22 Maastricht
23 A compact disc.
24 First child of English parentage born
in the Americas.
25 The Turin Shroud or the Holy
Shroud.